CAREFUL
leadership

How your leadership can create safe,
compassionate and effective healthcare

Dr D J Hamblin-Brown
MA BMedSci BM BS FRCEM

HCV Publishing

HCV PUBLISHING

Published by HCV Publishing
Mark Cross, East Sussex, TN6 3PA, UK.

First published by HCV Publishing 2016
as *The Art of CAREFUL*
Revised edition 2022

Original book design: Lou Millward

Typesetting by Kassandra Bowers / Lakazdi
Book set in Sabon Roman 9/13

The moral right of the author has been asserted.

ISBN: 978-0-9563833-7-2
ISBN: ebook 978-0-9563833-8-9
www.careful.cc

for Melene

CONTENTS

CONTENTS

Preface

The bulk of the first version of this book was written during September 2014. I remember the time clearly because I spent most of a two-week holiday in Majorca working steadily on the text, largely in isolation in the dining room of a rented house. Which, of course, sounds nice.

In reality, it was a difficult time. My wife had been told that the baby she was carrying had died at ten weeks gestation – the third time that something similar had happened in as many years – and we were waiting for this to be resolved either by a spontaneous abortion or, once we returned to England, through a surgical termination.

You might reasonably conclude that I should have been more attentive to her needs and less focused on writing. Don't worry, I am reminded often enough, but time seemed qualitatively different during that holiday, as if we were waiting between worlds. Writing seemed suitably liminal as we moved around the house and made occasional forays to a local beach.

When we returned to England, my wife accepted the necessity of a surgical termination. She was taken to theatre one morning, directly from the local "early pregnancy unit". She spent a few hours regaining her strength and balance and was sent home that evening. A couple of days later she began to bleed more heavily and by the following morning we knew that something was clearly wrong. We returned to the same department.

She was examined by a doctor who declared her fit to return home. A bit of peri-operative bleeding was to be expected. I remember both the inscrutable look on the faces of the staff and the trail of blood-spots on the floor as she left, sent home, a woman visibly haemorrhaging, shivering in the early stages of shock.

Thankfully, I was a senior emergency doctor. I took her directly to my own emergency department where she was scanned. She had 400 millilitres of fresh blood in her uterus – roughly ten per cent of her circulating blood volume. I still feel a surge of gratitude for the kindness shown by our emergency nurses during those few hours and for the competence of the doctors who treated her. She was admitted, given tranexamic acid, IV antibiotics and some fluids. Despite a fall in haemoglobin she avoided a transfusion and was discharged after a couple of nights.

That this extraordinary contrast in both humanity, and basic clinical acumen, could exist so close together in the journey of one patient, sums-up the reason for this book, namely the need to address very directly the importance of healthcare leadership in creating safe, caring and effective clinical services.

That the two groups of clinical staff could work in such close proximity and yet offer such different experiences and outcomes is, in my opinion, a shining example of the impact of first level leaders. First level leaders are the most numerous leaders, closest to the "base" of a traditional organisational chart. They are the people who most strongly influence the quality of care through their role-modelling and their support, direction and inspiration of the staff around them. Their leadership capability, more than their technical expertise, or any other factor, is critical to the quality of care delivered day-in day-out in busy departments across the world. It is towards these leaders that this book is directed.

I should stress that through this story I do not intend to find fault – either with the institution or with the individuals involved. I have had too much experience examining and unpicking the Swiss-cheese effects that combine and create serious harm to patients. Blame is neither a useful nor correct response. The systems of work which are created within each department by first level leaders are what need strengthening. It is these systems which persist as individuals come and go through these departments. I tell this story purely as a pertinent image to reinforce the overarching premise of this book:

> ... *first-level leadership is of paramount importance to patient care; it can be learned – and should be widely taught.*

A few months after this incident, I put the finishing touches to the manuscript, and then had the book typeset, which seemed an easier task than finding an agent and a publisher. By then, my enthusiasm for the project had waned – and so the book never really saw the light of day. The following year, I was promoted in my clinical work and then appointed to a Group Medical Director role in the private sector. In 2018, I left the UK to help lead an expanding group of hospitals and clinics in China. By that time, my wife and I were fortunate to have had another child – a fact which provides something of a happy ending.

But the China job, my most recent and most fascinating leadership position, ended abruptly because, well, because now it is 2022. The coronavirus pandemic rages across our world and we are in the middle – possibly only at the beginning – of a wave of suffering, death and disability that will be with us for years to come.

As a result, healthcare professionals are being been put under strain in ways previously reserved for war. I have no war stories for this period since I have taken the view that the world is better served if I am late to the battle than an early casualty. As a result, my clinical practice and my leadership positions have for the last few months been put on hold.

In that time, I have moved to create impact through med-tech* rather than my clinical work. And I have unearthed this book, which has been lurking in my subconscious and my hard drive for more than seven years.

On re-reading, I realise that it has many faults and is in some places seems somewhat out-of-date. It fails to draw on any of the many experiences and mistakes that I have made, and from which I have learned, during the last few years. It would undoubtedly benefit from a re-write – but my calculation is that better would then become the enemy of good.

What this book tries to tell, however inexpertly, is the importance of being both kind and rigorous. It may have been intended for a different time but perhaps this message is even more relevant now than it was seven years ago.

It is therefore with the firm intention to benefit as many of my fellow healthcare leaders as possible, that I commend this book into your hands, your mind and your heart. I hope that it can have relevance to your struggle to be a better healthcare leader, and to improve the care of your patients. Its many imperfections are mine alone. May its benefits give you support, encouragement and inspiration in this most difficult time.

DJ Hamblin-Brown
East Sussex
May 2022

* see *www.careful.online*

Acknowledgements

This book would not have been possible without the longstanding encouragement of my wife. Emily, your forbearance of my own behaviour, generally, is clear from the preceding story, and your support for all our endeavours has been both unending and yet tempered with realism and sound advice. I owe you a debt of gratitude for much else besides.

I would also like to thank many of the people who read and critiqued various versions of this book over the years: Jo Swinnerton, Nina Lyon, David Bond and Victoria Millar – you have all been hugely helpful at different stages.

Within the book itself, I have made reference to several inspiring individuals and friends, as well as many investigators, researchers, authors and practitioners. I hope that the passages in the book will stand in acknowledgement of my gratitude for your work. Like everyone else, I stand on the shoulders of giants.

My thanks also go to the many attendees and administrators who contributed to the "Art of CAREFUL" master classes that I have run intermittently over the years. From you, I learned a great deal; from your stories of success and failure and from your enthusiasm for excellence in patient care. I hope sincerely that – if this book ends up in your hands – you recognise some of your own contributions to it.

I also want to acknowledge the debt of gratitude that I owe to the many colleagues who have provided me with examples of great leadership over the years. Not all of you work in healthcare – but many of you do. We all recognise the superb examples of clinical and administrative leaders, without whose courage and persistence our hospitals and healthcare institutions would not run at all, let alone well. You are, as we are finding out during this pandemic, the heroes of this unwelcome war.

Finally, I want to acknowledge the dignity and courage embodied by my mother Melene, to whom this book is dedicated. In her final months, she was an exemplary patient, cared for by some exemplary people, most notably my brother Jeremy and my sister Jackie. From you, my family, I have learned most.

Thank you.

Acknowledgements

INTRODUCTION

CAREFUL leadership

Compassion binds us to one another.

– Nelson Mandela [1]

The body is big. And wet. The unconscious form of a half-drowned man is wheeled into the Emergency Room by the ambulance crew. Whether by accident or design – drunk, depressed or both – he's spent the night in the bilge of a rowing boat. He's blue. And half-dead.

Four of us heave his cold and heavy form onto the resuscitation trolley and begin our work. He is still breathing, but only just; a sound barely audible as waves on a shore. A feeble pulse, life's will to live, trickles in his neck. No blood pressure to speak of. He is cold as a tomb.

We set up a drip, warmed and pumped by a machine. We stab him in the groin to take blood. He doesn't flinch. Nor do his pupils react to the bright lights we shine at him. We record his heart with an ECG. We order some X-rays and request a scan of his brain. We insert a catheter. We cover him with warming blankets. The flurry over, we stand back to wait.

The patient is critically ill, and will probably die. He needs to be put on a ventilator to protect his lungs. For that, he needs the treatment and support available from the Intensive Care Unit (or ICU as it is more casually known). We call the intensive care team and ask for their help. We're told they're busy with several other, critically ill, patients. He can remain safely with us. If his condition worsens, he's in the right place and we can ring them back. We will have to wait before they can come and help.

I've been an Emergency Department doctor in this hospital for no more than a month. I'm still relatively junior and inexperienced so I am left to watch over him with some more experienced nursing colleagues. The patient is stable, but our concern grows as the time passes. He is barely alive, and is liable to deteriorate at any moment. We know that the warming blankets can cause a shift of chemicals within his bloodstream and precipitate a cardiac arrest. We stand by his side, watching the monitors.

Just then, a middle-aged man with glasses perched a long way down his nose comes up to my side and smiles. "Hello," he says. "I'm David. From ICU."

I feel a surge of relief. I thank him for coming so quickly and explain the situation as cogently as I can.

He nods, then says, "What's his name?"

I look blank for a moment, then tell him the name we found in the patient's wallet. This is all the information we have.

The ICU doctor nods, taking it all in, and then approaches the patient, leans down to his head and addresses him softly by name, reassuring him that he is now in hospital and that we are doing everything that we can for him. As the doctor begins his own examination of the patient, which he performs with meticulous fluidity, I hear him explaining to the unconscious man exactly what he is doing.

As I watch, I realise that this is the first time that anyone has addressed the patient directly during the time he has been in our department. Everyone, including me, has assumed that this patient is comatose, unable to sense what is going on.

The ICU doctor turns back to me, also addressing me by name, and we discuss the patient's condition and prognosis. We study the results of the patient's blood analysis, which shows that the patient is in poor condition. "He'll need some bicarbonate," says the doctor, looking inquisitively over his glasses at me.

"I'm not familiar with prescribing bicarb," I confess. I sense he realised this. So, for a few minutes, he explains and teaches me how to calculate and prescribe the right dose and the likely effect on the patient's blood results. We then discuss antibiotics and the fact that the patient needs to be on a ventilator before going for a brain scan.

After a few minutes, he returns to the patient and talks to him, again using his name. "We're going to give you some medicines which should make you feel better. We're going to help you breathe by putting a tube in your windpipe. To do that, we need to put you to sleep."

A few minutes later, with the help of another member of staff, the patient is anaesthetised and put on a ventilator. Not long after that, he is wheeled out of our department, accompanied by the ICU doctor and the resus nurse, first to the CT scanner and from there to the intensive care unit. I finish my paperwork and move on to the next patient. The entire episode was over in less than 30 minutes.

Later that day I was sitting in the coffee room during my break, discussing the patient with a colleague.

"Good to have Prof by your side," she said.

"Prof?"

"Yes, I heard ICU was really busy. I assume that's why Prof came to help out."

"I didn't know he was a professor. He seemed a really nice guy."

"The word 'nice' doesn't really do him justice – he's much more than nice. I tell you, if I was really sick, I'd want to be airlifted to his ICU, no question. He's one of my heroes. When I was in ICU, he taught me everything I know about critical care medicine and about how to run a unit." She paused and added: "And a lot about how to be a good doctor.

"What I really admire is the fact that he treats everyone with real kindness: staff, patients, relatives – all the time. He's never too busy. And yet, despite that, he's also one of *the* world-renowned experts in Intensive Care Medicine. He's regularly over in the USA teaching and liaising over research programmes. He has, quite literally, written the book on the subject. It's required reading in my view.

"But the most important thing is that we get really good results. Patients do much better on the unit than you would expect, given the type of patients we treat. According to the data, it's safer and better than in any of the neighbouring units that treat the same population.

"I reckon that if it weren't for him, this hospital would probably have lost its ICU long ago. He's published hundreds of papers. And his staff love him. In fact, as a tribute, they've named one of the rooms in this hospital after him."

"A tribute?"

She returned to her sandwich and then looked up. "Yes. He's retiring this year. It'll be a real loss."

For a few moments I reflected on my brief experience of this man, a world-renowned expert on his subject who had come down in person to help out because his colleagues were busy. I remembered the sense of relief that I felt, and how he had made me feel better about the situation. I remembered how he had addressed me by name and how he had listened carefully to everything I had to say. He had even taken some time to teach me something – without making me feel stupid.

What I remembered, above all, was how he had immediately started talking to our patient by name, explaining and reassuring, even though he was unconscious. That, I realised, had had a calming effect on me. For the entire time we were working together, I felt this doctor had been totally present for me and, more importantly, for my patient.

YOU

If you are a leader or manager who works in healthcare – and that includes most doctors and nurses, as well as those with "manager" in their job title – this book is written for you.

In the UK, where I work, healthcare accounts for over ten per cent of our domestic spending and more than a million people work in the health services – roughly one in every 30 taxpayers. The same proportions are true in most developed countries, and in the USA the numbers may be doubled.

Of this vast number of healthcare workers, the majority are leaders. This includes the more obviously senior managers – the CEO and the board, for instance – as well as everyone who has manager in their job title: ward managers, general managers, practice managers and so forth. Less obviously, perhaps, it also includes almost all junior doctors since, after only a year in the job, they are themselves helping to lead and manage the doctors who have just left medical school. It includes every qualified nurse who manages clinical support workers or students as part of their job. It also includes every shift manager, team leader or supervisor – and this includes tutors – in any non-clinical or allied health profession.

My definition – admittedly quite wide – is that if you are required to take accountability for someone else's work, you're a leader. And by my estimate, that's about 60 to 70 per cent of healthcare workers. That makes half a million healthcare leaders in the UK alone and maybe 30 to 40 million worldwide.

If you are one of these many healthcare leaders, please take a moment to congratulate yourself. You're doing a difficult job and you are likely doing it well, perhaps without much specific training in leadership. All leadership roles are difficult, in most part because there is no handbook that can teach you all you need to know. But healthcare leadership has particular challenges since we are trying to deliver a high quality of service to patients under circumstances that are both unpredictable and challenging.

Healthcare leadership can be particularly challenging because it often deals with highly charged emotional situations. You may think that emotion is restricted to the patient-facing professions, but if you are, for example, a biochemistry shift leader running a lab overnight, you will not be immune to the fact that healthcare is emotionally charged. If an essential analyser goes down, you can be sure that you will be reminded rapidly that "lives depend on getting it fixed". Dealing with the sick and dying, at however many steps removed, is a difficult business.

Leading healthcare services is also difficult because we are also of necessity consumers of these services. When one of our family falls sick we often come face to face with a service that is inadequate, uncaring, or merely inefficient. It can be disheartening to discover that we contribute to a service which regularly fails its patients.

Finally, healthcare leaders daily face the uncomfortable truth that there isn't enough to go around. The demand for healthcare appears unlimited, while resources are relatively scarce. A form of Moore's law seems to stalk everything we do: every few years we need twice the number of people, beds or appointments. Where healthcare ends, social care begins, and the dividing line between the two is rarely clear. As a result, you – as a healthcare leader – are always going to be asked to do more with less; to do more than is possible. How you deal with that, how you work with patients and staff to cope with these difficult boundaries and limitations, can be as difficult to manage as the care that you deliver.

Despite these challenges, I would wager that you strive hard at your work because you want to make a positive difference to patients. You try whenever possible to provide a safe, high-quality service. You know that the way you manage and lead within your own department, clinic or hospital has a direct bearing on the nature and the quality of the services that are delivered to your patients, and so you try to improve that service.

This book is about that. About *your* leadership. It's a manual, of sorts. Not one that will tell you exactly how to do your job, but one that may give you some ideas and pointers on how to deliver a better service to your patients and, crucially, to your staff. Leadership is primarily about helping people – your people, the staff you work with – do a good job. If they do a good job, you will have succeeded. So this book provides a structure that you can apply to the problems that you face in your day-to-day job and in so doing create an environment in which your staff can flourish and provide better care, whether directly or indirectly, to your patients.

ME

From my story about Prof, which took place a few years ago, it will be apparent that I'm a doctor. For half my working week I still work as a physician in an emergency department – A&E as we call it in the UK – dealing occasionally with very sick patients like the one I have just described. More usually, I spend my time listening to and advising patients and colleagues in situations where people are less unwell, but may nonetheless be anxious, exhausted or confused. I love this work. I love doing what I can to reassure and help the people who come to our department. The work may be occasionally stressful, but I am thankful to find it deeply rewarding.

But I wasn't always a medic. I spent several years away from medicine, working as a consultant and project manager helping multinational companies in the manufacturing, energy and utilities sectors to deliver large change projects. So, for the other half of my week, I now use this experience to work with healthcare leaders and managers from within the public and independent healthcare sectors. Through this work I try to help improve the way they, and their organisations, care for patients.

In an attempt to have the greatest effect, I have made the thrust of my work about helping these leaders find better ways to lead and care for their staff. My belief, backed up by studies within and beyond healthcare, is that staff who are well cared for do a better job. The clear implication for us is that the better we look after our staff, the better they will look after our patients.

What I have found, over 15 years of working in this field, is that leaders often become stuck. Leaders see the same old problem in the same old way, sometimes to the extent that the problem simply becomes part of the furniture, part of "the way things work around here".

Many healthcare leaders spend years working competently in the same role. Many come to accept that change comes from above, and that change will make things worse, and that "this is as good as it gets". Sadly, I find many of my clients and colleagues are depressed by their leadership responsibilities.

My sincerest hope is that this book can help to change that.

THE CAREFUL LEADER

I tell the story about Prof – who is, I should stress, not an amalgam of other individuals or some fictional character, but is a real, recently retired ICU consultant lauded by those who worked with him – because it was clear that even at the end of his career he was not stuck. He was fully engaged with his work, with his patients and with his staff.

The story summarises a leadership style that we find too rarely demonstrated by leaders in healthcare – especially, I am sad to say, by the medical profession. I recognise that this description of leadership is one particular presentation. I recognise that there are many other, equally valid styles and theories of leadership.[2] Some models are very theoretical. Others, usually advocated by hyper-successful individuals, often suggest the need for toughness, strength and emotional distance. In my view, this can be counterproductive.

Healthcare is a nuanced and complicated arena, populated by highly motivated, intelligent and self-directed individuals, in which situations requiring uncompromising individualism rarely arise. The image of the be-gloved surgeon regarding an X-ray and declaring "We're going in" is as far from the truth – and of what is desired or necessary – as can be imagined.

Healthcare leadership needs, in my view, to be the opposite of such unhelpful caricatures. We deal, in the daily round, with frightening and unpleasant situations in which both practitioner and patient may be uncertain and anxious. We need leaders who openly recognise, and work compassionately in, those situations.

As I've already suggested, it is the emotional complexity of the arena, for both patients and staff, which marks healthcare leadership out as particularly challenging. We must take this into account, even if we don't need constantly to verbalise it.

Research tells us that an enormous change takes place in the majority of healthcare practitioners, and especially among doctors and nurses, in the period between starting their training and the first few years of practice.[3] Most start out enthusiastic, altruistic and open. Within a few short years, many have become overtly cynical, seemingly uninterested, and often depressed. Junior practitioners take on the emotional characteristics and language of their older peer group and senior colleagues, many of which are negative and oppressive.

The fact is that you, as a healthcare leader, constantly influence your colleagues, especially your younger and more junior colleagues, more than you may care to acknowledge: each gesture, each throwaway remark, each choice of epithet, each attitude you strike, can have a far-reaching impact.

Such a simple act as identifying a patient by their condition can provide a retreat from emotionally challenging situations and perhaps, as it becomes habit, a stance in which the patient becomes objectified and eventually treated with disdain. Such forms of influence and their impact rest with you. Each time you speak, you encourage others to follow your example.

For this reason, in my leadership ideal I emphasise a combination of overt kindness mixed with something more focused and uncompromising. I characterise this as being both compassionate and rigorous. The word *careful* might be substituted for both characteristics: the empathetic quality that should characterise a caring profession and the attention to clinical and managerial detail that should characterise professional practice are two sides of the same coin.

We must not fail to recognise the humanity and fragility of the human frame and the human mind – our own, as well as that of our patients. If we don't recognise in both our staff and our patients the adage "there but for the grace of God go I" then we fail to recognise the very reason we do our job: to salve and treat the human frame and human mind as they inevitably fail.

And we must remain positive and supportive in the face of those failures. One day they will likely be our own. We must empathise with both our patients and our staff. As fellow human beings, that honesty is what they most need from us. If we are to be human, we must show compassion to ourselves as well as to those around us.

Yet we cannot simply emote. We must also provide a service that is both safe and effective. We need to do the right things by patients and we need to learn from our mistakes. For that – to provide an objectively balanced service that monitors itself and improves – we must be rigorous and, as much as possible our decisions must be driven by numbers.

Finding the balance between these twin aspects of rigour and kindness can be difficult and occasionally paradoxical. To give it substance, I call it CAREFUL leadership.

The word *careful* acts primarily as a strong reminder of the reason we take up healthcare in the first place, namely to care for others. It is easy, in the frenetic pace of delivering healthcare to lose this most basic fact of our vocation. But it also here acts as an acronym, the letters of which refer to seven leadership qualities discussed in detail at the end of this introduction. The qualities are: Committed, Active, Responsive, Energetic, Focused, Uniform and Leading. These qualities can also be considered as skills. They can be developed with mindful application and practice. I have written this book in the hope that you may develop these qualities in yourself.

EXERCISE 1: YOUR FAVOURITE LEADER [4]

In this chapter, I have shared with you a story of a leader that I have found personally inspiring.

Question 1: Ask yourself who is at the top of your list of inspiring leaders with whom you have personally worked. [5] This rules out Mahatma Gandhi and, most likely, your mother. It may also mean the list is short. Write down the qualities you admired in your favourite leader. Explain why you choose them. What was it about them that put them at the top of your list?

Please finish Question 1 before going on to Question 2.

Question 2: Think of all the people that now work for you or around you. Think, more generally, of the people who may look to you as a role model. Who looks up to you? Who sees you as a leader? Make a list if it helps. Visualise them. Now ask yourself this question: *How many of these people, when asked, would put you at the top of their list?*

Your Leadership Challenge

There is nothing more difficult ...
than to take the lead in the introduction
of a new order of things.

– NICCOLÒ MACHIAVELLI [6]

This book is a practical guide to CAREFUL leadership. Leadership inevitably revolves around delivery and the implementation of change. Discussions and thoughts about implementation may be interesting in themselves, but in the absence of something to implement are merely academic. Without some means of applying the ideas, models and tools presented in this book, they are unlikely to have a lasting impact on your leadership.

I would therefore ask you to select a particular challenge from your own current situation to use as a worked example while reading the rest of this book. In Part Two, I will refer to this often as "your leadership challenge". I will suggest exercises to encourage you to link the theory and models in this book to your own direct – and current – experience.

You may notice that in the exercise below it emphasises a *care* or *service delivery* challenge. I have found many people, when faced with this question, are tempted to isolate an individual as the problem they face. I would urge you to reconsider this, since you will likely find the challenge too narrow. We will have an opportunity to discuss the challenges of leading individuals in the Energetic and Focused chapters later in the book.

EXERCISE 2: YOUR LEADERSHIP CHALLENGE

What is the *care* or *service delivery* challenge that you would most like currently to address in your work?

Consider the issues that you face day-to-day. Which of them stands out as the one you would most like to solve? Write down the challenge as you see it in a few sentences – no more than a paragraph. Try giving this a title, beginning: "How to …?"

Now, in one or two sentences, describe what *impact* a successful solution to this challenge would have:

- on your patients
- on your co-workers and colleagues
- financially
- on you personally.

Whatever you choose, it is possible that you will need more than one attempt to find an answer to this question. It is common for leaders to begin by thinking of a problem they wish to solve only to discover that this is part of a wider problem and they need to broaden their horizons. Conversely, some people find they have cast the net too wide, and instead decide to concentrate on a single aspect of their original problem. Don't hesitate as you read this book to return to this exercise in order to review and re-state your leadership challenge. You may need to do this more than once, if you feel it needs further refinement.

The seven CAREFUL qualities

One man in his time plays many parts,
his acts being seven ages.

– W<small>ILLIAM</small> S<small>HAKESPEARE</small> [7]

The remainder of this book is divided into two parts. Part One contains some thoughts and some practical suggestions on what I have called the Art of Leadership.[8]

PART ONE: ART OF LEADERSHIP FIND THE FEELING

This covers aspects of language and psychology which I hope will contribute to a sense of positivity for you and your colleagues (and thereby also for your patients). These ideas are culled from different sources, all of which I have tried to acknowledge.

PART TWO: CAREFUL LEADERSHIP

Part Two is organised around the CAREFUL acronym: Committed, Active, Responsive, Energetic, Focused, Uniform and Leading. These are seven qualities or skills that I believe can be cultivated by leaders, with a bit of guidance and some application. My hope is that the individual chapters, which describe various concepts and models and provide some practical suggestions, will help you develop these qualities. These chapters are best tackled in the order presented, treating them as stages on the road to the implementation of your leadership challenge.

Below is a brief explanation of each of the chapters in Part Two.

COMMITTED: Create Alignment

Without support from your colleagues, your attempts to change or implement anything will not go far. This chapter helps you first consider how to define and quantify your goal and then offers some thoughts on how to generate commitment from others. Done successfully, this will ensure that you and other leaders are aligned in what you want to achieve.

ACTIVE: Manage the Workload

One of the primary challenges in any implementation is how to get things done. Initially, this means setting your own house in order. I offer some thoughts on how to manage your own time and to-do list and how to be clear about the actions that you and others need to take. The emphasis in the latter half of this chapter is on successfully managing meetings where decisions about actions are taken jointly.

RESPONSIVE: Learn to Learn

All organisational problems are interconnected. Your leadership challenge will sit within a complex and constantly changing system. You will therefore need to flex your implementation in the light of other factors and to respond positively to changes. Drawing primarily on recently developed approaches to patient safety this chapter offers ways to consider your challenge more systemically.

ENERGETIC: Develop Your Team

Your capacity to implement is in large measure down to your capacity to inspire and influence those around you and in particular your ability to build a team. This is sometimes disparagingly called "the soft stuff", but it is by no means nebulous. There are some simple skills and models that can be learned that will transform your approach to the people who look to you for leadership.

FOCUSED: Tackle Negativity

If there is one thing that will very quickly derail your ambitions, it is negativity from colleagues. This can cause conflict and undermine your team. Dealing with negativity is arguably the most difficult aspect of leadership. This chapter builds on the last by examining how you can define and promote positive behaviours. It also discusses some psychological games that people play. It offers some ideas on how to tackle these.

UNIFORM: Control Your Processes

Whatever your leadership challenge, improvement will necessarily involve a change to one or more processes – often called "business processes". You will need to understand these processes fully and communicate exactly what is changing and for whom. This chapter offers a way to think about processes: how to define, manage and communicate not just the processes themselves but also the management systems that control them.

LEADING: Aim for the Top

I maintain that you, and everyone around you, wants to work for a leading organisation – one that is either first or best in some way. We want to work somewhere where we can be justly proud. This seventh chapter offers some thoughts on becoming first-or-best.

A note on models and tools

I have mentioned models several times in the description of this book. I use models a great deal to help explain and embed ways of thinking. Models are visual aides-memoire; useful ways of thinking about a situation. They will help you to assess and solve problems on the fly, without having to refer to books or other materials. They are ideas that you can hold in your mind as you are confronted with a leadership situation.

Tools, by contrast, are intended to be printed out and used by you and your colleagues. They may take the form of, for instance, spreadsheets checklists, or presentation files.

Some of the models and tools are included in the book as diagrams, alongside their explanations in the text. To save you time, they are also available to download under a creative commons licence, from *www.careful.cc*, where there are many other resources for you to explore.

PART ONE:
THE ART OF LEADERSHIP

Watch your language

*The meaning of your communication
is the response you get.*

– NLP Presupposition [9]

I have been fortunate in my career to have received only one complaint from a patient. It came from a young woman who had been pushed from her bicycle by a car and had hit her face on the pavement. She hadn't been knocked out, she had some bruising and a nosebleed and some swelling around the mouth but no sign, in my view, of anything serious.

My judgment was that her injuries did not warrant an X-ray or a CT scan. I tried to reassure her that all would be fine and that what she needed was a hot bath to help her get over the shock and the inevitable whiplash. Although she didn't complain at the time, she was sufficiently unconvinced by my nonchalance that she paid for a private CT scan of her face.

This showed an undisplaced facial fracture. Although this needed no treatment and, I assume, healed without complication, her complaint about me was not simply that I had missed a fracture – which worried me as much as her – but that I had been dismissive of her. She was particularly upset that I had recommended a hot bath as a treatment. In my mind, of course, I had not been dismissive, I had tried to be reassuring but had missed the mark entirely.

This incident taught me a lot. I now always ask, before ending a consultation, whether the patient has any questions or concerns. I also learned that jocularity – while it can have a relieving effect in some circumstances – should be used sparingly. And I learned to read the signs. If a patient looks concerned, I now check. "You look concerned. Is there anything you're worried about?"

The quotation that starts this chapter – "The meaning of your communication is the response you get"[10] – resonates throughout our line of work. As leaders and clinicians, the language we use is the only tool we have to influence those around us. Whatever we think we mean, the effect of our language can only be judged by what we observe in others.

However much I intended it to be reassuring to the injured cyclist, the meaning of my communication was, to her, dismissive, lacking both good clinical judgment and compassion. The communication was no better than its outcome.

We don't all have to receive such an uncomfortable lesson in order to adapt our communication habits. We can also take time to reflect on the impact our language may have on those around us. Changing language habits can be difficult, but doing so can profoundly change the impact we have on others. Leadership is in large part about influence and impact, and language is the medium in which this takes place.

TOP LANGUAGE TIPS

Within the individual CAREFUL chapters in Part II of this book I have made a few particular suggestions about the use of language within the area under discussion. Here, I am going to offer three "top tips" on the language of leadership. These are not meant as condescension. I offer them only as food for thought.

TIP 1: Don't complain about the traffic

One of the prevalent problems that I have found in working with healthcare leaders is the blocking effects of one particular senior member of staff. His terrible resistance to all good sense and his deafness to all entreaties is the cause of much heartache. The staff member in question is referred to by all who know him by his initials "TM".

I have even had conversations with senior hospital leaders who have told me: "It's impossible to get things done around here. I've tried but TM won't do anything." The blocking effect of this individual is pervasive. And TM is mean too. Given half a chance, he'll readily take away well-deserved perks and ruin any work–life balance. He's clearly a menace to the organisation.

TM, if you haven't already guessed, is "The Management". This is an example of a language habit – and not one that helps the user. The Management does not exist any more than the fictional TM. There are leaders, there are human beings, there are processes and there are conversations.

When TM comes into being, those processes and conversations are embodied into a thing that can be blamed even though TM is neither a human being nor a leader. Even though TM is a fictional character, once one person invokes him, he becomes the perfect excuse for everything else that doesn't happen. When people come to believe in him, he becomes a truth.

Complaining about the management is like blaming the weather. It's just not a good excuse. There are plenty of other similar phrases: "this organisation", "this place", "the board". If you use such expressions, you won't hear what your listeners are thinking. If you hold any leadership position where they think *you* are "this place" you should assume that *you* are "TM".

It is simply not a good idea to encourage anyone to the think that bosses are idiots or charlatans – either individually or collectively. If those around you think that you are a leader, they will assume that you are responsible for making changes, for persuading others, and adapting to new ways of working. And they'd be right. The likelihood is that if you badmouth your colleagues – however indirectly – your colleagues will badmouth you.

So, my top tip is not to blame the organisation for anything. If you can't persuade TM to change, your responsibility is to explain why not. His response is not an excuse in itself.

Or, to borrow from a famous quote about being stuck in traffic: you are not hamstrung *by* the leadership.

You *are* the leadership.

TIP 2: Learn to be wrong

I was once with a non-medical colleague having a discussion related to our business. My colleague suddenly became irritated and said "Every time you insist on being right, you make me wrong." He was clearly exasperated.

The incident struck me forcibly as a truth that I'd never really appreciated. I thought we were merely having a discussion – jointly attempting to get to the right answer. I was taking a position and was expecting my colleague to argue the case from his side. What I hadn't appreciated was how this created a contest. Who would win? Who would lose?

As a doctor I have been taught over many years to diagnose and treat. This usually means making a judgment on limited information and taking a decision based on that judgment. Making such decisions requires me – and all my fellow doctors – to have faith in these judgments, and be willing to justify and argue our position to our peers. It's a habit I had acquired without realising it.

But in this case, we were taking a management decision, a leadership decision. And by trying to ensure that my point of view would prevail, I was forcing him to admit defeat. Not a great feeling for anyone. Had he not made this clear – if, perhaps, I had been his boss and he felt unable to challenge me – he might have left the room feeling mildly humiliated and less like interacting with me again. Repeated enough times, across an organisation, such incidents can have a withering effect on the ability of teams to work effectively and creatively.

"So what?" you may ask. "Surely taking decisions based on arguments, right and wrong, is the only way to get to the bottom of a difficult problem. These people need to man up and get stuck in." This may be true in some circumstances, but if you do think that, hear me out. There are drawbacks.

One serious drawback is that once you've taken a position – decided, if you like, to be right about something – it can be difficult to undecide. Many medical errors have been compounded by people continuing to insist on a point of view in the teeth of evidence to the contrary. And when politicians refuse to resign, it's the same principal at work. We don't like to change our minds.

In his seminal work *Influence: Science and Practice*, Robert Cialdini, Professor of Psychology at Arizona State University, talks about this effect. He calls it *Consistency and Commitment* – a characteristic of human behaviour visible in much of his research. This shows that when we, as human beings, have decided something, and more particularly if we say to others what we have decided, it becomes difficult for us to change our mind. Our attachment to a consistent image of ourselves includes maintaining – often at high cost – our opinions, our judgments and our decisions.

There is an important conclusion for your own leadership: you should stop trying to be right. In any given conversation, unless the subject under discussion is your personal speciality *and* you've had sufficient years of experience to be the reigning expert in the room, you are very likely wrong.[11] By rapidly deciding what is right you risk painting yourself into a psychological corner. By standing your ground, you will then make other people wrong and thereby alienate them.

Decisiveness is not a crime – far from it – but you will do better to keep an open mind until an agreement is built. If you spend much of your time making rapid clinical decisions, this can seem unnecessarily difficult. Below are three language tricks that can help.

Build Consensus with Conditional Assertion

There is a marked difference in hearing "This is the case" and "It's possible this is the case" or "Do you think this is the case?". The first of these statements allows only for contradiction. The latter two, by contrast, allow people to challenge you indirectly. You'll find out what they think more readily and this can help to build consensus. We'll talk more about this when we talk about facilitation in the Energetic chapter.

Widen your questions

If you want to know if someone agrees with you, a simple "yes", "aha" or "sure" just won't suffice. As with a problem in mathematics, they need to show their working. If you want to know whether someone agrees with you, use open questions to ask for their reasons: "Tell me why you prefer that option?" works better than "Do you agree?". If you want commitment to complete a task, don't ask "Will you do that by Thursday?", ask "When can you get that done?". These differences are subtle but important. We will return to this in the Active chapter.

Acknowledge your fallibility

"Is there anything I've missed?" or "I really could be wrong here" helps create a level playing field in which others can challenge your leadership. Many errors in healthcare have been made because junior members of staff didn't feel able to challenge their seniors. Assume that you've missed something and someone will help you out. Assume you're right and they'll probably watch you fall.[12]

TIP 3: Enquire, acknowledge *then* advocate

I learned one of the most powerful lessons of my career while working as an advisor to a leadership team. I was trying to persuade a client to my point of view about how we should run some training sessions. I was sitting in an office shared with a colleague with many more years of experience in the field. He was at his computer, with his back to the conversation. I spent over an hour trying in vain to make a case for some change with my client. Eventually we reached an impasse. I just couldn't get the client to see it my way. My colleague turned around at that point and asked if he could join the conversation. "Can I just ask a question?" he said. He then posed several questions and said little as he listened attentively. He spent a few moments outlining the point of view I had spent the last hour painfully elaborating. My client brightened, saying that this was exactly what he had been saying all along! I nearly fell of my chair.

The meeting ended shortly afterwards in smiling agreement. "How on earth did you *do* that?" I asked afterwards. My colleague smiled and said, "Listening. Mainly."

Steven Covey's book *The Seven Habits of Highly Effective People* [13] has sold tens of millions of copies. It's a book about leadership, primarily self-leadership, which identifies ways to make yourself more effective as an individual. His first habit is "Seek First to Understand". He shows how finding-out what other people are thinking is the first lesson we must learn if we are going to influence others. What other people tell you is their context; it is within their context that we must intervene.

Two of my suggestions above, namely that you use conditional assertion and more open questions, are both examples of seeking first to understand. By inviting others to give their views, you are helping to bridge any differences between you and others, rather than drive such differences out of sight. To make this practical, I have learned a more general rule. Let us divide our language – what we say to people – into three types of utterance: enquiry, acknowledgement and advocacy. You can influence and persuade most effectively if you use them in that order.

Enquire first

Enquiry is the use of questions that authentically seek to find out what the other person thinks or to establish facts you can agree on. Try to use open questions, which start with "What do you think of …?" or something that seeks out their point of view. Guard against asking any question that starts with "Why?" – it tends to imply accusation. To avoid defensiveness, rephrase a question such as "Why are you late?" into "What time did you get to work today?", which seeks to establish the facts. Avoid leading questions that presuppose the answer: "Was the traffic bad again?" is not an enquiry.

Acknowledge second

Acknowledgement is telling others that you've heard what they say, repeating back to them or agreeing with them in some way. Acknowledgement is important, because it reinforces that you are listening. Saying "I realise the traffic is bad at this time of day" means that you've heard an excuse for being late and have not dismissed it. We know from our own experience that talking to someone who does not appear to be listening is frustrating. Acknowledgement diffuses this tension.

Advocate last

Advocacy is explaining what you think and your point of view. Advocacy is our primary mode of talking, most of the time. When we speak, we usually intend to tell people what's in our minds. When you next hear an argument listen for the phrase: "But what I'm saying is …". This is an attempt to repeat a point of view – further advocacy – in order to reinforce it. I call this the "Do you speak English?" form of argument. If they haven't understood you the first time, just shout louder. The problem with our default setting, advocacy, is that people won't hear you unless you've heard them – which is why it comes third in this list. Advocacy is only possible once you've heard someone's point of view and acknowledged it. Once you've done that, it may be possible to assert that "It's important to be on time" or even "I need you to leave extra time in future to allow for traffic".

In summary: listen first, let them know you're listening and only then put your point of view.

Incidentally, someone once asked me what would happen if everybody did this; wouldn't we just get bogged down in questioning each other, like a group of overly polite people trying to get through a door without anyone going first? My answer is that a group of people listening to each other gets a lot further a lot faster – or, to use the analogy, someone rapidly goes through the door by invitation, without a scrum of people all shouting and trying to barge their way through at the same time.

Soothe the inner animal

*No organism can afford to be conscious of matters
with which it could deal at unconscious levels.*

– GREGORY BATESON [14]

Have you ever stayed awake at night, turning some problem over and over in your mind, getting hot under the collar, repeating to yourself all the ways you're going to right a wrong? Have you ever fantasised, in a half-dream state, about how you're going to stand up to your boss, or perhaps a staff member, and girded yourself: this time – *this* time you're going to tell them exactly what you think? And then you find yourself, the very next day, passing polite conversation with that same person, saying nothing, not word about how you felt in the heat of the night.

There's no need to be embarrassed by any of that. We've all done it. This chapter offers some thoughts about where all of that comes from, and why it's important to you as a leader.

Many writers and thinkers have proposed explanations for how the mind works, from the Five Skandhas of the ancient Buddhist texts to the neurotransmitter models of contemporary brain scientists. They all agree that the human is a complex beast, troubled by a kaleidoscope of conscious thoughts, emotions and sub-conscious drives.

Since leadership is about people, and therefore about the way that humans and human minds engage with each other, the way we construct our theory of other people's minds is critical to how we lead. I am not going to put forward an explanation of my own here. I will instead outline two metaphors of mind provided by two experts on the subject.

RECOGNISE YOUR INNER ANIMAL

The first metaphor has been made popular by two academic brothers in the USA, Chip and Dan Heath, in their bestselling book *Switch: How to change things when change is hard*. In this model, the mind is like an elephant with a rider.[15]

The elephant is immensely strong, capable of hugely useful and powerful things, but also easily spooked. The elephant is your emotional mind. It is powerful and hard to train in the right way and in the right direction. If poorly managed, it can do a lot of damage. The rider, by contrast, is clever and thoughtful and able to plan and learn, but physically weak by comparison.

Together they make a great team, but the rider and the elephant need to be handled in different ways. You, as a leader, need to recognise that your fellow human beings have two sides: a rider that you can argue with logically and sensibly, as well as an elephant that you must motivate by coaxing and encouraging, but without spooking it. In short, when working with others, you must take care to consider, and cater for, their emotional elephant. We will return to this in more detail in the Committed chapter.

The second theory is from Steve Peters, a British psychiatrist and renowned sports psychologist who has coached many British athletes to Olympic medal success. This theory is set out in his book *The Chimp Paradox*.[16] Peters suggests that, much like the elephant and rider, we are part-human and part-animal.

In Peters' account, we are part-chimpanzee, an idea he says is borne out by the physiology and anatomy of our brains. Sometimes our chimp takes control, which makes us think, talk and behave like, well, a chimp. The chimp has a mind that has been honed by millions of years in the jungle. It is tribal, emotional and focused on the present, rather than the future. The chimp is paranoid and fearful and full of every emotion available, from rage to fear, from hatred to lust. Above all, it is self-interested. It is in charge of our flight, fight or freeze reactions.

The human part of our mind, on the other hand, has only a fifth the strength of the chimp. It has a much shorter evolutionary history. It only gets an opportunity to talk, act and think in a human way if the chimp is either settled or asleep – in other words when we do not feel under threat.

Peters also points out that the human mind requires more sleep. The chimp is the insomniac in the relationship and can be often found, up all night, screeching about wrongs done and imagining revenge, until the human wakes up and takes over, dealing, we hope, more sensibly with the reality of whatever situation has wound up the inner chimp. This explains why we lie awake at night imagining how we will throttle the person we greet then cordially the very next day.

When chimp-mind keeps us awake at night and our human-mind deals calmly with the daytime reality, all is well. When, by contrast, the opposite occurs and the chimp takes over unexpectedly during what might otherwise be a calm, daytime exchange between colleagues – an event dubbed an amygdala hijack [17] – the effect can be terrifying for everyone involved.

You'll quickly notice the similarity of these two models. They both have merit. Personally, I like the elephant for its more sedate and positive nature, its immense strength and power. Motivate the elephant, this model says, and we can move mountains. The chimp, by contrast, is a bit less lovable, even if his unpredictable simian nature – with its tendency to ruin our lives at a moment's notice – might seem a little more recognisable.

Peters' point is the same as the Heath brothers. We need to understand and manage our own personal animal/human divide if we are going to manage our lives effectively. If we don't understand our dual nature, chimp or elephant behaviour can take over, with disastrous effect – eating the wrong foods, being lazy, having extra-marital affairs, running away from problems, falling apart under pressure, having road rage, to name a few.

The human, or rational, part of the mind is then stuck with the consequences of this sort of behaviour, and has the unenviable task of explaining it when things have calmed down.

What, you may be asking, do all these subconscious animal metaphors have to do with my leadership? Aside from providing an insight that may help explain some of our own habits and contradictions, the overall theory that we are part strong and emotional animal, part conscious human also explains much of the behaviour of those around us. Those with a yen for Freud will be familiar with the metaphor of ego, superego and id; the chimp and elephant metaphors work in a similar way.

As a leader, you must recognise that the emotional side of each one of us – be it elephant, chimp or id – needs to be managed and soothed. You and those you lead need to feel safe and settled if we are going to be productive and caring. The animal part of our mind is easily frightened, easily takes offence, is easily distracted by issues of territory and status. It very easily takes over and acts against our overall best interests and, most importantly, against the best interests of our patients.

It is no surprise that fear on the part of the carer is one of the common themes that emerge from the stories of professionals treating patients with disdain or cruelty. If we feel threatened or damaged by the environment in which we work, we will be less likely to care for those around us. Caring – and healthcare as a whole – is a product of the human mind and its capacity for altruism.

To ensure that we, as humans, care for each other, we need to see that the chimp is not activated or the elephant is not spooked by the work environment. Creating a calm, non-threatening, non-spooking environment is the task of leaders. The chapter on kindness will consider this in more detail but first we need to think about how we, as leaders, can soothe the inner chimp and motivate the inner elephant of those we lead.

There is no single way of doing this, and no simple way either. All inter-relational situations are unique and complex. However, there is one word that neatly summarises everything we need: *positivity*.

GENERATE POSITIVITY

Positivity does not mean spin – putting a positive gloss on things, pretending things are good when they're not. Elephants and chimps spot such nonsense a mile away and will turn against you if they think you are trying to con them. I have no doubt that this explains the visceral dislike and poor reputation suffered by many politicians.

Nor is positivity the same as telling people The Truth As I See It. Being straight talking – for which I usually read unreceptive – is usually the last thing your colleagues want from you. Talking about how much work needs to be done, or what pain needs to be endured before the good times, is not much help either. It doesn't create a gut feeling of warmth and possibility. Chimps are basically lazy and elephants can shy away from anything that looks scary. Emotionally, we don't like to work hard – certainly not harder than others – and we definitely don't like pain. In fact there are a lot of things chimps and elephants don't like: strangers, work, surprises, cold, boredom and change top a long list.

Positivity means finding, acknowledging and nurturing helpful emotions in those around you, making people feel connected with each other and with you. It means uncovering the drives that give us a sense of relatedness to others.

Chimps and elephants like continuity, friends, warmth, exercise and familiarity. When these are in place our human rider has the opportunity to thrive and provide care to others. We work well with people we have come to trust but worry when trust and friendship are lacking in our environment. That may be because we are new to a job or there is high turnover in our team. People leave when there is too much change (a vicious circle that is sadly too common in healthcare). If our boss makes us nervous, we definitely won't work well – as we shall discuss in more detail in the Energetic chapter.

That is not to say that helpful emotions need always be upbeat. I recently worked with a group of theatre managers, and together we watched a harrowing film about the effect on a family of a death in surgery. The distress we all felt and the sense of compassion we shared for the family proved to be a motivating factor in working together to improve safety in theatres.

Positivity is generated when you help people connect and feel a sense of relatedness with each other. The way in which *you* can do that is by creating a sense of relatedness between *yourself* and others.

STRIVE FOR 5:1

"But I am already a positive person" you may think. "This is no problem. Everybody likes me!" Sadly – and many years research backs this up [18] – the odds are against you. Most people don't like or respect their boss, or any of their leaders in fact. Unless you are actively doing something about it, most people probably don't see you in a positive light.

To uncover some of the reasons for this somewhat depressing fact, it is worth considering these conclusions to some leadership research. [19] These can be summarised as follows:

In order to believe that you have a positive relationship with someone, you need to have a 5:1 ratio of positive to negative – or – neutral interactions.

Let me explain this a little further. A negative interaction would be, perhaps, getting a ticking-off for being late or not delivering on an action or something even smaller – a sigh that implies you've not done a good job. A neutral interaction could be simply delegating a task or saying a perfunctory hello in the corridor without stopping for a chat. A positive interaction, on the other hand, might be a friendly chat in which you ask about the children, or talk about the football. Or it could be a conversation during which you are thanked or acknowledged in some way. Or it could be a simple as an affirming smile.

The reasons for this are made easier to understand in the context of the chimp and elephant metaphors. We are naturally wary of others and we are tribal. We know about tribalism from our school days. We know how important it is to be in with a crowd, rather than be an outsider. And we all know how much effort is required to get in – and how painful it is to be excluded. This whole system is based on fear. It's threatening. We cope with this inherent tribalism at work because, for the most part, our human is in charge. But we are nonetheless strongly affected by our emotional judgments; you can't shake a gut feeling. Positive interactions make your elephant or chimp feel in, rather than out.

EXERCISE 3: HOW'S YOUR BOSS?

Think for a moment about your current boss.

- Do you feel you have a positive relationship? Now cast your mind back over the last few days or a week and add up the interactions that you have had. Classify each one as positive, negative or neutral.
- Do you have a 5:1 positive ratio? Does your answer fit with your overall judgment?
- Now repeat this exercise with one or more people you consider to be your leaders.

Now look the other way. Look at each of the people that you lead – not just direct reports, but people who you influence.

- Ask yourself the same question. How many positive, neutral and negative experiences, *from their point of view*, do you think you have had?
- Work out how many have a positive, and how many a negative, ratio.

The 5:1 ratio problem – and it is a problem, unless you spend a *lot* of time being positive – is a profound issue for your leadership, especially if you are new to a leadership role. We all know that first impressions count. This is often put down to the primacy effect, a term used in psychology to denote the cognitive bias in which people recall the first pieces of information far better than information received later on. In my view, the phenomenon of first impressions is also related to the 5:1 problem.

If you have, for example, three negative or neutral interactions early on with your new staff, you have to have *fifteen* positive interactions fairly quickly before you can claw your way back.

What's so important about having a positive relationship with your staff? Can't you be a good leader without that? I would say no. Let me give you an example from my own experience. An independent healthcare company with whom I worked appointed a new CEO. Within a few days all the office chatter was concerned with how hapless (and tactless) he was. After a few weeks, stories of ineptitude were circulating as open gossip: "Did you hear what he said to me ...?" Within two months a petition was sent to the board explaining the concerns of senior staff. Within six months he was gone. His experience, salary and seniority counted for nothing.

The people around you won't go out of their way to support you unless they see you in a positive light. Without their discretionary effort, none of your ideas or plans will find traction. Everything you try will be stressful and you may not understand why people are being difficult and things are going badly. You won't, in short, be able to make a success of your job.

Having the word "manager" in your job title doesn't make you the boss. It is those you lead who give you your authority and only when they accept you, can you really claim it.[20] The autobiographies of many powerful people, including very senior politicians, will attest to this being the case.

DON'T GET BLAMED

A phrase that I encounter frequently when working with leaders is "bullying".[23] There is, of course, such a thing as bullying, where an individual is intentionally targeted, unfairly and repeatedly and is damaged by the experience. True bullying constitutes abuse and must be stopped.

However, in most cases when I've been told about bullying it has been nothing of the sort. On closer inspection, it turns out to be ineffective leadership; assertiveness from people who are not well liked. Leaders who do not have positive relationships – who don't have that 5:1 ratio – make things worse when they try to assert control. Their attempts to get things done and to push hard simply tip the ratio further in the wrong direction.

They cause the inner elephants of those around them to pull in the other direction – or, as in the case just outlined, they cause the chimps to push the offender out of the tree.

Part of this syndrome of negativity, which is so often labelled as bullying, revolves around the perception of blame. Being blamed is a negative experience. As a result, any negative experience can be confused with blame – and often is. Holding someone to account for something – which is a clear leadership responsibility – can be a negative experience for someone. Every time you, as a leader, tell someone that they mustn't do something, or that they have done something against accepted protocol, or that they must be investigated because of an incident, however justified your views, you are piling up negative experiences. If those negative experiences run towards a 1:1 ratio, you're going to be accused of bullying.

All of this, of course, is a matter of balance. But it is important to know where the balance lies. It lies much further towards positivity than we generally realise. And if you want to defuse or avoid the false label of bullying, there is only one way to do it: pile up the positivity.

Sounds difficult? It's not. The next chapter explains three very simple things you can do.

Learn to be positive

*People will forget what you said, people
will forget what you did, but people will
never forget how you made them feel.*

– Maya Angelou (attr.) [21]

This chapter describes three positive habits that you can begin to develop tomorrow.[24] However, before we start on this list, they come with a word of warning: your chimp or elephant will resist all of these strongly – at least to begin with.

The first two of these, in particular, will make you feel exposed and uncomfortable. You will therefore find a thousand subconscious reasons to avoid doing them.

To soothe the animal part of your mind, which is telling you not to do any of these things, I have a simple suggestion. Only do it once. Or rather, tell yourself that you will do this only once. If you tell yourself you'll do this *every day*, then your elephant will spook out, and your inner chimp will start screeching uncontrollably. Do it once. See how it goes. If you enjoy it, you can repeat it – that should be a deal your inner animal will accept. My hope is that you'll find these three habits worth repeating. Before committing, just try it and see.

MAKE NEW FRIENDS

About six months ago, I took a blood sample to a lab. Not, you may think, a very exciting thing to do. It was only when I was standing amid the mass of humming machines and the small army of white-coated technicians that

I realised that I hadn't been in a hospital laboratory before. At least not one as big as this.

I was suddenly amazed. The size and complexity of the operation was astounding. I realised that I order blood tests without really thinking most of the time. I just hit a button, post the blood bottles into the pod and an hour later a series of figures appear on a screen.

The reality of the process that occurs in that intervening hour is remarkable. I was in the lab for long enough to get a blood gas result – about five minutes – and in that time I was able to chat to one of the senior technicians who was helping me.

I explained my sudden awe at his domain. He smiled wryly and told me he'd been there for over 15 years and was very proud of the service they provided the hospital. Not, he said, that anyone else appreciated it. I told him they did a great job and then left. From then on, if I passed him in the corridor or in the canteen, we smiled and acknowledged each other.

What I had inadvertently done was something that I have been urging leaders to do for years. And my colleague's smiling reaction, and our continuing sense of relatedness from that brief encounter, reinforced what I have long held to be true – that with a short visit to someone else's workplace you can create a sense of positivity that long outlasts your brief visit.

This is your first positivity habit. For want of a better phrase, I call it doing leadership rounds. You're a leader, and what everyone wants from a leader is visibility. If you don't believe me, think of George W Bush's absence after Hurricane Katrina. It's true that you're not the leader of the world's largest economy. But an invisible leader is derided, whatever their role. The greater your leadership responsibility, the more visible you need to be.

While this fact is widely understood, few leaders actually make a habit of being visible. Practically no junior leaders bother. And although every senior leader will tell you "Oh, I visit all parts of the organisation, I'm always meeting people". You could counter with: But are your visits positive?; How are your visits received?; Are they seen as inspections or Royal Visits or attempts to catch people out?. You have to be careful not to upset people by turning up and talking about problems. Whether you are a junior or senior leader, you need to make sure that your visits are positive affairs.

It's helpful if people genuinely like you, as we will discuss later. To ensure that they do, you have to make sure that you make people feel good about the work they do. And it doesn't matter if you're a small cog in a very large machine. Providing you don't turn up in the middle of a crisis, you won't be derided for coming round to tell people they're doing a great job. Everyone is proud of what they do and reinforcing that will always go down well.

There are some reasonable objections to this: you're not going to be welcome just barging into private meetings or into someone's office uninvited. Start with the places where you know you will be welcome and then consciously work outwards from there. If you know that, for security reasons, they have a locked door – the pharmacy for instance – you may need to make an appointment. Just ring someone in the department and say you'd like to see how their place works. I can guarantee that anyone who has pride in their work won't say no.

If you're a senior leader, of course, you're allowed to go where you want. That's one of the perks of the job. There's no barrier to you getting off your chair, getting out there and meeting some new people.

Once you are there, however, you need to generate some positivity. The key to this is not to concentrate on problems. Concentrate on what is going well. Quint Studer, a renowned healthcare leader from the USA, suggests you ask three questions: "What is going well?", "Who is doing a great job?" and "Are there any tools and equipment you are lacking to do your job?".[22] These are really great, positive questions, although you will need to make these questions your own. I personally like "What's the good news around here?" – it acknowledges that there might be some bad news somewhere, but that we're ignoring it for the time being.

The useful thing about the second of these questions, "Who is doing a great job?" is that you can generate even more positivity by acknowledging their work right away. You should also mention who recommended them. This will foster goodwill between the two.

The last of these questions – about tools and equipment – may sound odd, but it can reveal some real quick-wins. For one client of mine, a department had been labouring without air-conditioning for months despite following all the usual purchasing protocols. All the staff had been stifling in the heat, until a quick call from the chief financial officer cut through the red tape and the problem was sorted. Senior leaders can do this sort of thing, so they should. It makes for a very positive visit.

In summary: walk the floors and ask some positive questions. I promise, you won't regret it.

SAY THANK-YOU ... PROPERLY

I worked with a hospital recently that installed a staff barometer – a seven-question ultra-simple staff survey, run monthly and sent to all employees. One question we asked was: "In the last month, have you been thanked or recognised for doing a good job?" The answer yes, every month, hovered around 30 per cent. That meant that in any one month, less than a third of staff were acknowledged for the work they were doing. Is this a problem? I believe it is.

We know ourselves how important it is to be recognised – it's a way of creating relatedness between people and thereby soothing the chimp/elephant. We immediately like people who take the time to thank us and, as we will discover, being likeable is a powerful leadership attribute.

Thanking people is your second positive habit.

However, just saying thank you to someone's face is usually not enough. We tend to forget it or dismiss it as too casual. Written thanks, on the other hand, is much more powerful. The written word can be kept, re-read and shown to others.

So, I recommend that, as well as thanking people orally, you also spend a few moments each week writing at least one thank-you letter to your colleagues. Personally, I don't like email – it's almost as ephemeral as speech – but use it if you prefer. Just remember that there is simply no substitute for a hand-written note.

You can also combine these two habits. In your leadership rounds, you should ask "Who is doing a good job?" – or whatever equivalent phrase comes naturally to you: "Who's your star player?" is a sporting alternative. If you spend a few moments discovering why they are doing a good job, you can use this specific information for a written thank-you letter. Return to your desk and write out a few lines by hand. If someone recommended them, mention that person. You get double the positivity that way. Writing a short thank-you letter takes less time than buying someone a coffee and will reap many more benefits.

The old saying goes that "There is no such thing as a free lunch" and yet thanking people in this way is free. It's a free lunch of positivity for any leader. It costs nothing and it has a visible effect on those around you. I've heard some people complain: "Why should I thank people just for doing the job they're paid for. No one ever thanks me!" There's a double standard in this objection which recognises that we all like to be thanked and acknowledged but because no one does it, no one should. Take no notice.

One final objection to counter about thank-you letters is that in healthcare there are hierarchies and boundaries between departments. It's possible that you don't think you have the *right* to thank someone because they are more senior than you or it's interfering in another department. This is a chimp/elephant objection. The way to counter it is simple: spend a few moments considering how you would feel if you personally received a hand-written note thanking you for something you'd done.

BROADCAST SUCCESS

I was wandering past the noticeboard in my department the other day and I noticed that, without fanfare, one of the managers had put up a small notice on the board about our recent patient opinion data. The graphs showed the last two months of replies – about 500 of them – as well as some of the comments received.

The thing that struck me was that of the five possible responses about how well they thought we were doing, over 90 per cent of patients had ticked *Strongly Recommend*. More than nine out of 10 patients had strongly positive opinions of the service we are providing. I'll repeat that for emphasis. These patients did not just tick the *Recommend* box, they chose *Strongly Recommend*. Ninety per cent is, as I'm sure you will agree, an outstanding result.

Did I know that? Had anyone mentioned this? Had anyone celebrated this? Had we received an email or a newsletter telling us how well we were doing? Sadly not. The only thing in my pigeonhole was a request to answer a patient complaint.

Healthcare is, in my view, terrible at celebrating its successes. We spend so much time diagnosing problems, as if they were diseases, that we forget the good stuff. For 90 per cent of the time we do outstanding work for truly grateful patients. Whether it is processing blood samples for our colleagues or providing physiotherapy to patients, we spend most of our time doing a very good job.

It's true that there are variations within and between healthcare services that are unacceptable. It's true that there are terrible examples of avoidable harm – the rate of harm which must be tackled – but for the most part we help patients and they are grateful.

If you take a moment to look for it, you have all the necessary material around you to create huge amounts of positivity. If I asked you to write down ten things that your area or department did well, I doubt you would have difficulty. Whether it be on efficiency, outcomes, safety, patient satisfaction or staff development, you would be able to find a statistic that demonstrated that you and your colleagues are doing a great job. When did you last tell anyone in your department, let alone outside it, about these facts? How often, for instance, do you tell your patients about how well your department works? When I tell some of my patients how many patients we treat per day, they are often genuinely surprised (I suppose it's possible they thought we were all twiddling our thumbs).

We can also share good news about our colleagues, celebrating the qualities of our fellow-workers – awards they may have won, research they have published, qualifications they may have achieved. All this lends weight to a culture of positivity – helping push our interactions towards 5:1.

This, then, is the third and final positivity habit that every leader can use. Studer calls it "talking up". Talking up is about finding and celebrating positive stories about our work and our colleagues. It differs from empty spin, which our elephants and chimps would spot a mile off. Talking up is about finding genuinely positive things to talk about, not to the exclusion of the problems we may face, but to counter them, to remind us that we mostly do a fantastic job, often in difficult circumstances.

Telling people positive stories is uplifting for both parties. We need to hear these stories as a counter for our chimps/elephants who may otherwise see the world as challenging, or depressing. I'm not suggesting that we spend all, and every, day endlessly congratulating each other. We just need to tell each other the good news stories. There are plenty of them out there and your job as a leader is to seek them out and tell people about them.

EXERCISE 4: JUST DO IT

It is likely that you will resist these habits, so write down three things:
1) a part of your workplace you can visit
2) a person you think warrants a thank-you letter
3) something great about your own part of the organisation.
Tomorrow do this: visit 1, write and send a thank-you letter to 2, and tell as many people as you can about 3. If you get a positive response, repeat.

Above all, be kind

Three things in human life are important:
the first is to be kind; the second is to be
kind; and the third is to be kind.

– HENRY JAMES [25]

In May 2009, a patient by the name of Kane Gorny was admitted to a hospital in South London. Within 24 hours of his admission he had died of thirst.[26]

Kane was a young man who had been suffering from brain cancer. After long years of treatment, soon after his 21st birthday, he was given the news that he and his mother had been longing to hear: surgery and radiotherapy had successfully removed his tumour. He was given the all clear.

He still faced a long recovery and his continuing care was complex. Every day, he needed to take a particular drug, Desmopressin, because the cancer had affected that part of his brain that regulates fluid in the body. The cancer had gone, but had left him with a lifelong legacy of drug treatment to stop him from becoming fatally dehydrated. The part of his brain that regulates fluids – the pituitary gland – also had an effect on his bones. They were more brittle and vulnerable to fractures. Nonetheless, he kept fit and he was a keen football player. In May 2009, he sustained a fractured hip and was admitted to an NHS hospital in South London.

He was admitted under the care of the orthopaedic team, led by a senior consultant and attended to by numerous doctors and nurses before his surgery. Routine assessments were made, routine care given.

But Kane was not a routine patient and despite the consultant detailing his rare condition in the notes, the vital medication Desmopressin was not prescribed. By the time Kane reached the operating theatre despite appearing fine, he was already in big trouble.

There are many checks, counts and briefings in a modern day operating theatre, all intended to ensure one thing: do the correct surgery, safely, on the correct person. If the surgeon, who was not, incidentally, the consultant, had picked up and read the notes of the man he was about to operate on, he might have realised that catastrophic omissions in his care had been made. But he did not, and the opportunity was lost.

He would later say to the investigating coroner:

"My role was just the operation, I thought that had all been sorted out and assumed everything had been put in place."

The hip replacement was a success. But when he returned to the ward, the young man's condition worsened. He began desperately asking for water, a request granted initially by the nursing staff.

But he soon became agitated and aggressive, a symptom of his clinical decline. He was becoming more and more thirsty – and with his increasing thirst he became more and more desperate.

He started shouting and becoming aggressive, demanding water and even, at one point, calling 999. The police arrived but were ushered out by the ward staff, who explained that Kane was merely being difficult.

As his thirst intensified, Kane became desperate and eventually started to hallucinate and rant.

The carers on the ward became defensive and began to withdraw their care, becoming blinkered to his clinical situation and believing him merely to be an aggressive 21-year-old with an attitude problem.

Kane's mother had been in contact with the ward and reminded them of his Desmopressin, explaining his condition to them, but all they saw now was a difficult patient and a situation spiralling out of control.

Another consultant, not the admitting consultant, attended the ward to assess the situation. He recalls to the coroner;

"I told him I was a consultant, but he then said 'Oh, well if you are one of the consultants you are not going to listen to me.' I said, 'I may well not' – in hindsight, it may have been inflammatory."

Inflammatory it was. And true. His intervention did little to improve the situation. The medical notes remained unchecked, the drugs that could still have saved the young man's life remained unprescribed.

Later, and with a steady decline in the young man's condition, the surgeon attended the ward once again and this time prescribed sedating medication, knocking him out cold.

"It's a poor excuse, but I was in the middle of a busy clinic," he said to the coroner. "My main concern at the time was safety."

After he had been sedated, the young man was left in a side room, with no further prescription of care. No fluids, no observations, no further concern. The nurses who were there to care for him feared waking him and decided to omit his monitoring.

The next day, he died of dehydration.

By withholding his usual medication and failing to give him any fluid, the nursing and medical staff charged with looking after him had, in effect, conspired to kill him.

The subsequent investigation and coroner's inquest detailed these extraordinary failures towards Kane and, subsequently, to his family. They are a matter of public record. His story was a tragedy: a preventable and wholly unnecessary death.

And yet Kane's death was not a symptom of an unsafe hospital. In 2009, the NHS Trust in question was regarded as one of the safest hospitals in the country, receiving the "Larger Trust of the Year" award and ranked by the auditors Dr Foster as the fourth best hospital out of 146 NHS Trusts in terms of overall safety. Kane was being cared for in one of the safest hospitals in the world.

Kane's death was also not entirely a failure of systems or processes. It could be argued that a full reconciliation of his medication was not done pre-operatively and that this was the root cause of the problem. But that could have been done at any point in the story – that it was never reconsidered further contributed to his death.

To understand how such a drastic failure could have occurred in one of the world's safest and most sophisticated hospitals, we need to understand what has happened at the level of human interaction – at the level of empathy and clinical concern – and how this marred and undermined the clinical commitment and skills of the staff involved.

What was it that caused Kane's death? It has much to do with a lack of *careful* leadership. Ultimately, in my view, it resulted in a failure of kindness.

KINDNESS IS NOT JUST ABOUT BEING NICE

This book is about healthcare leadership – your healthcare leadership. I am therefore taking a few pages to reflect in some detail about the nature of healthcare and its relation to kindness. The model that I am going to present here was developed over several years by Andy Willcocks, currently the senior clinician and Chief Nursing Officer at the Lister Hospital in London.[27]

Healthcare is a uniquely human activity, as far as we can tell. Chimps, for instance, cohabit but never collaborate.[28] An overarching human trait is to work for each other's benefit in groups whose members demonstrate some measure of altruism or group-mindedness. It could be argued that healthcare – looking after the sick and dying – is fundamental to the cohesion of larger groups. We might even say, by extension, that healthcare is one of the foundations of human society. Providing healthcare is based on kinship – the recognition that a human being is part of our group – a word that shares its roots with the word kindness.[29] Healthcare is kindness in action.

Why, you might ask, do I use the word kindness rather than compassion, which is perhaps in wider use? Compassion implies a desire to alleviate suffering and requires a degree of empathy. Kindness, by contrast, is a little wider and more indefinite in meaning, encompassing generosity, sympathy and compassion among other things. Indeed, I would venture that most kindness is driven by compassion, so they are closely linked. In my view, the word kindness lends itself better to describing the particular behaviours that this book aims to develop.

The definition of kindness that Willcocks offers is a combination of two characteristics. The first and most obvious is empathy – a sense that you feel *with* the patient, rather than you simply feel *for* them; that you understand their predicament because you can feel yourself in their shoes, and you therefore act accordingly.[30] We do unto others as we would wish others do unto us.[31]

The second characteristic is clinical concern. This is healthcare specific. It is this aspect of kindness that sets it apart from mere compassion within a healthcare setting. Clinical concern is the desire to help the clinical situation – to recognise sickness and generate the desire to treat it correctly. We learn and develop our clinical concern more formally within the healthcare setting.

Kindness comes about, therefore, by seeing the patient as a person, for whom we need to feel empathy, a person who has a disease or condition that we need to treat. Using this definition, it is clear we must balance the two. If we have an imbalance between empathy and clinical concern – an excess of one at the expense of the other – then we can fail our patients.

Too much clinical concern at the expense of empathy describes the archetypal unfeeling specialist who is concerned only with blood results or surgical technique. The fact that such clinicians have no time for patients' feelings means they may miss important factors or cues, and so reduce a patient's capacity to communicate or express their decisions.

My favourite example from my medical school days is that of a surgeon who placed his handkerchief over a patient's face during a ward round in order to stop them speaking, but there are other less extreme examples that I witness every day in my clinical practice. When the disease eclipses the patient, the patient suffers.

Too much empathy, on the other hand, without clinical concern, is also dangerous. This is typified by the overly conscientious nurse who brings tea, toast and a magazine to a patient's bedside, tucks them in, holds their hand while cooing over photos of grandchildren, but fails to notice falling blood pressure and a rising pulse, signs that they may be deteriorating. One of my senior clients – a nurse of several decades – witnessed this very scenario while visiting his father on a ward only recently.

These two extremes are simply that: extremes. We must all find the middle way, where empathy and clinical concern are balanced. I was recently in a theatre when the surgeon – quite unexpectedly – entered the anaesthetic room and struck up a conversation with the patient before and, indeed, during, their anaesthetic.

"I was taught to hold the hand of my patient as they fall asleep," he told me. "That way, I can be 100 per cent sure it's the right patient on the table." Eyeballing the patient forms part of his own personal checklist, which we will discuss in the Uniform chapter. But he also said something that touched me: "Often I'm the only person here they recognise, having seen me in clinic. So they find it reassuring during what can be a fairly nervous time." Clinical concern (this is the right patient) balanced with empathy (this is a frightening place) makes for a moment of real kindness.

If you, as a healthcare leader, are going to ensure that your patients get the right level of care – the right degree of kindness – then, like this surgeon, you will need to ensure that you and your staff are able to balance empathy and clinical concern. And that's not easy because …

GOOD PEOPLE DO UNKIND THINGS

We ask healthcare professionals to engage in this balance of clinical concern and empathy every day during long shifts. As patients, we rightly expect that every nurse, every doctor, every person we come into contact with in a healthcare setting will be lovely to us and respond to our suffering effectively, but also with empathy.

Working on a busy ward, staff are expected to look after scores of patients every day and to do so with warmth and tenderness, yet with an eye for every clinical detail, every minute of every hour, every hour of every shift, all year. Willcocks calls this requirement to be continuously both empathetic and clinically concerned our "Duty of Kindness".

THE THREE KILLERS OF KINDNESS

This duty of kindness forces workers to develop defence mechanisms that help them cope with this continuous pressure. They develop a range of adaptations that allow them to distance themselves from the suffering that surrounds them.[32] In addition, healthcare organisations and healthcare leaders allow circumstances and culture to develop in a way that works against kindness. Together, Willcocks says, these create the three killers of kindness: fear, fixation and fatigue.

Fear

Fear works against caring. It is arguably our most powerful emotion. In extreme circumstances it changes us entirely. It creates the fight, flight or freeze response which, in the jungle, might save our lives but which, in the controlled environment of civilisation, can be destructive. Fear activates our inner chimp, and spooks our inner elephant.

When our inner animal is panicking, the human/rider can't concentrate properly on the empathy and clinical concern necessary for healthcare. The physiological changes induced by fear cloud our decision-making, impede our physical skills and change our temperament.

Fear also changes what we think is important.[34] It can make us both compliant and complicit with delivering poor quality care. Eventually, chronic, low-level fear will desensitise us completely, stunting our capacity for both empathy and clinical concern.

The problem is that healthcare is necessarily scary: patients deteriorate and threaten cardiac or respiratory collapse; we elect to do inherently dangerous or painful things to our patients, invading body cavities, injecting drugs, transfusing blood; and patients behave in frightening ways through delirium, dementia or psychosis.

But our jobs can become needlessly scary too: the negative reactions of our seniors can make us cautious or inept; a culture of blame puts us on guard; threatened or actual changes to our team or the environment unnerve us. It's not surprising that our chimps or elephants can be on high alert for most of our working lives. This is bad for us, and bad for our patients. Fear causes us to become withdrawn, clumsy and forgetful. We stop caring about others and start prioritising caring about ourselves.

The conclusion we should draw from this is that we healthcare leaders should remove as much fear as possible from our organisations, because our patients will suffer if we don't.

Fixation

If we work somewhere for a long time, we take mental shortcuts. I don't mean that we don't do our jobs properly, I mean the opposite – we become so good at them, we stop thinking. We make assumptions and switch off.

We can also become entrained into the attitudes and behaviours of the group with whom we work. Fixation is the second F. We develop a fixed view of our overall situation, of how things should be done or of how our patients should be treated.

Like fear, this capacity is very good for humans. It helps us to fit in with our troop. It ensures we can adapt. It also allows us to do repetitive tasks without having to re-learn things. But fixation has a downside too. In healthcare we can become fixed in how we view and treat our patients.

I have worked in departments where anyone with a drug habit is known as a … actually, that's unprintable. Staff become used to referring to patients by their condition ("We've got an abscess on the table and we're waiting for a hemi"). The recent Mid Staffordshire scandal in the UK included extreme examples of fixation on organisational priorities over patient care.

Less obviously, we can all become blind to new treatments or innovations. "That's just the way we do it round here" can blind us to ways that would improve patient care.

Fatigue

Finally – and this requires less explanation – fatigue is the enemy of kindness. Not only does fatigue erode our capacity to engage with good humour, let alone empathy, but it also impedes our clinical decision-making.

In my first year as a doctor, I remember working nearly 100 hours in a week. I was unable to remember simple prescriptions, or even take a history from a patient. I also remember the anger that I had to suppress towards my colleagues and my patients.

Thankfully the absurd working hours of junior doctors has been curbed in the UK, but we do still ask a lot of many of our staff, particularly if they work night shifts. Moving from day working to night working and back again creates a huge physical and psychological burden on staff and undermines their capacity to provide good care. Even now, rotas that are compliant with the European Working Time directive can still be punishing for the carer, and consequently dangerous to the patient.

And even ignoring these extremes, we do our patients no justice if we turn up to work tired. In the UK, over 40 per cent of people report getting less than six hours sleep a night. The situation is similar in America. This sort of chronic sleep deprivation works against our ability to give good care.[33] Good leadership is ensuring that you get enough sleep yourself, and that you encourage your staff to do the same.

The result of the three Fs is that they change people. People who enter the caring professions with the best of intentions and the purest of motivation become slowly ground into a state where they no longer act with kindness. Fear, fixation and fatigue can turn the most open-hearted student into a cynical, narrow-minded and potentially dangerous employee.[35]

It's your job to ensure this doesn't happen.

ACTS OF KINDNESS NOT JUST AT THE POINT OF CARE

The question is: how do we prevent ourselves and our colleagues from becoming unkind? The answer is not straightforward. To rediscover kindness when we have unconsciously become unkind may require a major shift in world view. Even if we can recognise the effects that fear, fixation and fatigue have wrought upon us, such a change in attitude may seem impossible. We may need to become different in ourselves, to approach our work more openly and be more willing to be affected by the suffering around us.

FOUR KINDNESS STRATEGIES – ACTS

This book cannot adequately describe such a shift. What I can offer is a summary of four strategies – or ACTS, as suggested by Willcocks – that may help unlock our kinder selves.

Ask

Explore what you are doing and why you are doing it. The first stage in any interaction, whether with a patient or a colleague, can be to simply to stop and check. Ask yourself: What is important here? What sort of carer or leader do you want to be?

As an example from my own work, I know that I am prejudiced against certain types of presentation. When I pick up a set of patient notes for the first time, my eye is drawn to the one or two-word summary of the reason the patient has presented to the emergency department. Some phrases make my heart sink. To counter this I always ask myself, before greeting the patient, how I want this consultation to be, for the patient and for me. It takes me no more than a second to remind myself that treating all similar presentations as all the same is simply fixation.

Such reflection can be done in many different ways: briefly in longer sessions, alone, in group or with help. Asking yourself the question is an attempt to uncover and undermine our own unhelpful attitudes.

Choose

Decide what you want to be, how you want to act. Consciously choose how to express the values and behaviours that reflect the way you want to be as a leader, or as a carer. This is not necessarily easy, as anyone who has tried to diet or quit smoking will attest. Our ingrained habits are hard to break, especially when under stress. Nonetheless, the clear water of your intentions will eventually wear away the stone.

To continue my own personal example, I choose to be kind and open with my patients. Asking has given me a moment to reflect and, as a result, I have a moment – again, no more than a second – to choose my approach, my tone of voice, my motivation. I remind myself that every patient I see has come to me in some degree of distress and I am there to help, if I can. Any other attitude: impatience, disdain, irritation, will destroy me. It may sound odd that I should do this with every patient, but I know it works. I consciously decide. I choose.

As an aside, it is worth noting that most organisations actually take a lot of time to write up and publicise their chosen values. My view is that this is an attempt to do the choosing for the staff. My values may include honesty, but being told by my employer to adopt honesty as a value doesn't help me choose. Choosing is personal. Remember that you, as a leader, need to help people choose, not impose your own choices on them. We will return to this in the Focused chapter.

Transform

Allow your experience to change you. Get close enough to your patients and to your staff to let their experience become real for you. Doing this profoundly affects your own capacity for empathy. Getting to know your patients and getting to know your staff is imperative if you are going to be kind, and encourage kindness in others.

I work in an environment where we see patients for such a short period of time that it may seem impossible for me to be transformed by my interactions. To let myself be open to this, I make a point of asking every patient a personal question which I hope will bring me closer to them. I talk with the older generation about the war, and their part in it, and compare it with my parents. Younger patients I ask about work or children or travel. And with that opening, I find a moment of humanity. I can empathise, and they can feel it.

For instance, a few days ago I was at the bedside of a 90-year-old ex-soldier who had been married to his wife for seventy years. She suffered from severe dementia, and was in a care home where he had visited her every day for 14 years. She had had a funny turn and, in his hurry to get out of his house, he had fallen and was now in A&E. He was white with worry that she was dying while he was in hospital. He gripped my arm. "I do so love her, you see". We were both crying.

The consequence of offering and receiving such moments of humanity is that it lets you in. Into the person that is in front of you. Or perhaps more accurately, it lets you out. Out of your own protective suit. The suffering of others – whether mental anguish or physical pain – is a reminder of our own physicality, our own mortality. And as such it is sobering, and it connects us.

This doesn't have to be about patients. One of my senior nursing colleagues has a severely disabled son. Knowing this, and hearing about their struggle gives me the opportunity to empathise and her the opportunity to talk openly. This is not arrogance. It's connection. Your colleagues can transform you.

Share

Finally, work with others to improve their capacity for kindness. Tell others about your experiences and seek out theirs. Without reflection, we deny ourselves the capacity to learn and without learning we become fixed.

The importance of sharing the emotions involved in caring underlies the Schwartz Center Rounds that are now gaining ground in both the USA and the UK. In 1994 Kenneth Schwartz, a 40-year-old non-smoking healthcare lawyer from Boston was diagnosed with lung cancer. In July 1995, he wrote movingly in *The Boston Globe* [36] about his experiences. His ten month ordeal, he said, had been punctuated by moments of exquisite compassion. "The acts of kindness," he wrote, "have made the unbearable bearable."

The centre which bears his name is dedicated to uncovering and promoting compassion in healthcare. The Schwartz Rounds are designed to encourage caregivers to share the human side of their work.

Schwartz Center Rounds are a place where people who don't usually talk about the heart of the work are willing to share their vulnerability, to question themselves. The program provides an opportunity for dialogue that doesn't happen anywhere else in the hospital. [37]

Research [38] demonstrates that they have a positive impact on participants and, indirectly on teamwork and patients. Participants that I have spoken to personally describe their effect as profound. For many people, sharing is difficult and unfamiliar. Having a structured and formal approach can be beneficial.

However, we don't have to use such formal mechanisms to reflect and share our experiences. We can and should do this informally, with colleagues. We will return to the importance of reflection when talking about types of conversation in the Energetic chapter.

You may also notice that only one of these four activities – Transform – is at the point of care. All the others engender kindness by working with yourself and others away from the patient. Kindness – and improving kindness – is not just at the point of care.

TAKE CARE OF YOUR STAFF

Of course, acts of kindness are not restricted to those in the caring professions. Society is based upon the exchange of kindness – of kin-ness – throughout all our lives. Parents, siblings, friends and acquaintances all exhibit kindness towards us every day, even if we may often take this for granted. And we have all had experiences where a stranger has shown us unexpected kindness. Kindness is all around us.

So our own, overt, acts of kindness need not be focused exclusively on our interactions with patients. Nor should they be, as the nineteenth century American author Henry James suggested, in the quote that starts this chapter, kindness should pervade our lives and our work. In fact, I find it incongruous to witness a clinician being fastidious with a patient and then turn on a junior colleague to humiliate or browbeat them for some triviality. The discrepancy suggests to me that any empathy towards the patient is inauthentic.

Which means we can, and should, choose to be kind to our colleagues as much as to our patients. I would recommend it. It pays dividends to spend time *asking* and *choosing* how we wish to be with our colleagues. Remember your favourite leader, from the exercise at the beginning of this book. How were they to you? Did they exhibit concern for your career, your progress, your skills and competencies? Did they also seem to care how you were doing personally, and seem to understand your feelings – perhaps when you were quite junior? If so, and I have heard many examples of this, they were being kind. They were showing a balance of concern and empathy.

And why stop there? If you are going to be kind to your patients and your colleagues, is it such a jump to show a degree of concern and empathy towards the people with whom you interact on the street, or in your other areas of responsibility? I'm not suggesting you take a personal interest in the woes of every shop assistant you bump into, but there is no harm in showing them concern and, above all, empathising with them. Asking the postman who delivers your online parcel how they are doing doesn't increase transaction time, but it does increase transaction value – for them and for you. As I have heard quoted by Matthieu Ricard, a physicist turned Tibetan monk: "We only have one heart". Practicing kindness in one area of your life, rubs off in the others.

I say all this with confidence, because the research is very clear.[39] Patients want kindness from their healthcare interactions more than anything else. Schwartz knew that. And I would wager that it is what you want too. And there are more benefits too. People who demonstrate kindness to others are themselves healthier and happier. If you show kindness to others, you can benefit as much as they do.[40]

Perhaps the most powerful treatise exhorting healthcare professions to open themselves up to the importance of kindness in healthcare is *Time to Care* by Robin Youngson, an anaesthetist brought up and trained in the UK. He describes the dehumanising culture of hospitals and medical training and the terrible effect it has on both carers and patients. His discovery of the extraordinary power of compassion has led him to found *Hearts in Healthcare*, a global campaign aimed at transforming our approach to patients.[41]

Kindness is perhaps the most important quality anyone can cultivate as a human being. For you, as a healthcare leader – with the huge impact you can have on staff and patients alike – it is essential.

PART TWO:
THE SEVEN QUALITIES OF
CAREFUL LEADERSHIP

COMMITTED
Create Alignment

The moment one definitely commits
oneself, then Providence moves too.

– W H Murray [42]

I once bought an old car made by Saab. Prior to that I had known only one person with a similar vehicle, so although I knew the model, I didn't imagine there were many on the road. After buying it, I seemed to be surrounded by them. No trip, however short, seemed unaccompanied by a genial wave from another Saab owner. Such changes are a common experience for us all; we see the world differently depending on where we are mentally.[43] Buying a car is a big commitment so it has an effect on what we see.

In my view, it is this tendency for us to see the world differently, depending on our current mental state, that explains the observation by William Murray a Scottish mountain climber and writer; your luck changes once you've committed to something. By deciding definitely to do something, we find – seemingly by coincidence – that opportunities present themselves, newspaper articles appear on the subject, other people mention that they have relevant skills to help and so on. We also find almost miraculously that we can find the time and energy to put into a project. Ask any first-time marathon runner where they got the time to train and they'll usually say "I just stopped watching so much TV" or something similar. In other words, they prioritised. If you're committed, things happen.

However, from a leadership perspective, commitment is not just a personal matter. Leadership means engendering commitment in other people. That is the trick, and it is the reason commitment is the first of our seven leadership qualities. Leadership, at its root, involves encouraging other people, often a group of disparate people, to do a job in common. The group in question may be your entire organisation, or it may just be your personal team, but the challenges are the same.

The commitment you seek from others may be broad – "excellent patient care", for instance – or narrow, such as "use this new booking form". If your challenge requires, like the first of these, a wide commitment from many people, then you are clearly in the business of creating a shared purpose. It will come as no surprise that this requires those involved to have an emotional attachment to the outcome. What may not be so obvious is that creating an emotional attachment is also important for smaller goals, such as using a new booking form. Like it or not, creating a commitment in others is an emotional business.

What you will also find is that commitment creates commitment. So, if you have an organisation that is committed to excellent patient care and you can convince people that using a new booking form will contribute to that excellent patient care, then commitment to the booking form will come for free. Once you have succeeded in creating sufficient emotional attachment, much of the other work is made easier. Commitment will carry you forward.

When considering your leadership challenge, I would therefore urge you to consider how you might create wider levels of commitment rather than narrow ones.

Commitment has an extraordinary power. Seemingly normal people if committed enough can do extraordinary things, as attested to by stories of local heroes, both honoured and unseen. Take Terry Fox, for example, an otherwise unremarkable Canadian boy diagnosed with sarcoma in his right leg. After undergoing a high, above-knee, amputation, he committed to running across Canada in an effort to raise awareness and money for cancer research. He ran 143 marathons on consecutive days, covering 3,300 miles before his disease returned and killed him. His legacy is a cancer research institute that is among the best in the world and has donated $600 million to cancer research worldwide – an amount far in excess of Terry's original goal of raising just $1 million. [44]

It would be hubristic to suggest that we can all make such an impact if we were only to dig deep and really commit. Terry was a truly outstanding individual and an extraordinary athlete. I use the story only to point out that individuals can achieve much more than we might believe. Whatever the goal, commitment is the essential ingredient. Which means that if we, as leaders, can develop our own commitment, we can achieve things we might not have believed possible. And if we can bring others along with us, we can achieve even more.

This chapter is about how to garner such commitment from others. The broad areas I am going to cover are about Motivation (where I will be talking mainly about elephants), Measurement (where I will be thinking more about riders) and Influence (which will draw on interesting research from advertising). I'll finish with some brief thoughts about language and meetings.

EXERCISE 5: RECOGNISING COMMITMENT

Think of the commitments you have made in your own life and the effect that these have had on your life. Reflect on those occasions when you knew you were committed and ask yourself:

- Was there a particular event, moment or person that caused you to become committed?
- Was your sense of commitment sudden or gradual?
- What did it feel like?
- Did your sense of commitment feel different from other levels of intention or desire?
- Were you able to communicate your commitment to others? If so, how did you do it?

MOTIVATE THE ELEPHANT

I mentioned the elephant and rider metaphor in the Introduction (see page 38) and I'm going to return to it now for a large proportion of this chapter. Using this model, it is clear that we must address both rider and elephant if we are to attain commitment. We must start with the elephant since it is the strongest member of the team.

No commitment is real without the support of our inner elephant, that vast subconscious self that does all the heavy lifting. Knowing that we *should* do something is never enough, because the rider alone – our conscientious rational self – is simply too weak. The failed dieting or exercise regimes that litter all our pasts are testament to that.

The elephant is emotional. It's non-verbal. It can't be persuaded with words and charts. It can't read PowerPoint – in fact after a few slides the elephant is either ready to charge, or fast asleep. If we want to garner commitment from others, we need to engage them emotionally. By the way, if you're suspicious of this as an approach, just ask yourself this: When you were last asked to make a change with which you strongly disagreed, how did you know that you disagreed? Was it because the maths was wrong? Or was it because you felt irritation and frustration boiling up inside you?

If you're going to get people to commit, you need to find a way to make them *feel* like committing. In their book, *Switch*, the Heath brothers unpack three ways in which we can motivate the elephant.

FIND THE FEELING

This means appealing directly to the emotions that drive the elephant's behaviour. I mentioned earlier the harrowing video that I shared with the group of theatre managers.[45] This may sound like an extreme example of finding the feeling, but in healthcare, patient stories have an important role to play. I once talked to a head of midwifery who described how a newborn baby had died unnecessarily on their ward. The baby's observation charts had not been filled in assiduously and its deterioration had been missed over the first 24 hours. The hospital recorded the mother's harrowing testimony on video, in which she described how she had seen her firstborn die slowly in front of her, unnoticed by staff who were allegedly too busy to record the baby's vital signs. The video was shown to all the staff in the maternity unit. Within days an audit of neonatal observations showed, for the first time, absolute 100 per cent compliance. No training, no posters, no emails, no exhortations from senior leaders. All that had changed was the staff's emotional connection to the importance of neonatal observations.

"Finding the feeling" can take many forms. One of the best ways of getting staff to understand what needs to change is to put them – as near-literally as possible – in the shoes of the patient. Simply asking staff to accompany a patient on their journey through a hospital or clinic can totally change their view (so confusing, so many questions!). Asking members of staff to interview patients or other staff members about their experiences can have the same effect Arranging visits between departments can create a sense of relatedness. Anything that helps other people get to the heart of your leadership challenge will help.

Just remember, however convincing they may seem, charts, statistics and bullet points won't work. The elephant just ain't interested in that sort of stuff.

SHRINK THE CHANGE

Elephants are easily spooked by large-scale change and can't think long-term. It can be counterproductive to explain how radical, how far-reaching, how rapid and how large are the changes that you are about to suggest. Root-and-branch reform makes elephants very uncomfortable. What they like is small, easily understood steps, thereby making the change simple and straightforward and therefore easier to commit to. If you can find one simple thing that needs to change, use this as a lever for other things.

One example from my own experience is trying to implement new guidelines for a Clinical Decisions Unit at one of my hospitals. The problem we faced was that we had to ensure that the patients that were placed in this overnight ward were suitable and that unsuitable patients were not admitted. The obvious – and elephant-spooking – way of doing this would be to develop a clear set of standard operating procedures, guidelines and checklists, present these for approval and train all staff in their use. All of this seemed such a huge undertaking in a busy unit that very little work had been done on it – and inappropriate patients were still being admitted. The solution was to implement a one-page pro-forma, which needed to be signed off by the doctor who would have to take charge of the patient. This change had the desired effect almost immediately. There was still work to do, but with one form, we had already made the change more manageable.

GROW YOUR PEOPLE

Elephants are herd animals – they like to stick together. One of the most powerful ways in which we can create commitment is by encouraging a sense of self-identification with the goal. In short, people like me are doing this. Healthcare, in my experience, is the perfect place to use this approach. Healthcare professionals readily self-identify as part of various sub-groups (think uniforms, and Royal Colleges). This can make it difficult to encourage staff to identify with their employer. Instead, what we find, almost universally, is a sense of pride that healthcare workers have in their professional standing and qualifications, and in the importance of their professional development and behaviour.

When considering your leadership challenge ask yourself how your ambition aligns with the needs of the various professional groups. One of the examples I use to illustrate this is the adoption of the World Health Organisation's *Five steps to Safer Surgery*, often referred to as the "WHO checklist" – a mechanism for improving the safety of patients in theatres. We will discuss this in more detail in the Uniform chapter but I will mention at this point that many doctors were initially very resistant to taking up what seemed to be unnecessary extra time checking and re-checking the patient's identity and surgical site. Now it is more common to find that surgeons and anaesthetists consider it their professional duty to undertake these steps properly. These once unfamiliar routines are now seen as being synonymous with good medical practice. Although in some cases it has taken several years, the checklist has now become closely linked with notions of professionalism. It is this identification of the checklist with good medical practice that has made a difference.

EXERCISE 6: WORK WITH THE ELEPHANT

Consider your own leadership challenge. Ask what emotional connection you want your staff to feel with the change you are proposing.

- How does it link to something that is really important to them?
- How can you generate an emotional connection between your staff and the challenge that you are facing?
- How can you make the change seem manageable?
- How can you help staff identify with the challenge?

Remember that patient safety and the patient's experience remain – underneath all the busy–ness of daily activity – the primary motivators for healthcare staff. If you can find a link between your challenge and either of these things, you're probably off to a good start.

DIRECT THE RIDER

Having first dealt with the elephant we must now approach the rider. While the elephant is hugely strong, it doesn't have much foresight. For us to commit entirely, we must also understand our ambition in human terms. What exactly are we expecting? What is the outcome we are planning? Where are we headed? What does this *mean* exactly? In other words, we must direct the rider.

This is where we tend to start, our default position. When we want to persuade someone to do something, we often rush to direct the rider before adequately preparing the ground. Which means we are familiar with this form of persuasion. But beware. Even if we have spent time motivating the elephant, statistics, logic and reasoning may cause the wrong emotional reactions. So here are three ways – again from the Heath brothers' book *Switch* – that are worth considering. These build on the hard work you have already done, in order to direct the rider without spooking the elephant.

POINT TO THE BRIGHT SPOTS

We are imitative animals; humans love to copy. And imitation, as we all know, is the sincerest form of flattery. So before you start, it's worth working out who is already doing what you want to do well. You may find that you're already very close to something or someone world class – and that you just need to uncover this gem. Explaining to your staff what good looks like may be easier if you can use a common referent: we want to be like so-and-so. It's worth trying to find out who is best at whatever you want to do.

In my own speciality of Emergency Medicine there are several examples of first-class operations. The Homerton Hospital has one of the best-run moderately sized emergency departments (it got an outstanding rating from the regulator). For a larger trauma centre, Kings College Hospital has the best reputation in the UK. When anyone asks me how to improve the performance of their own emergency department I advise them to send members of staff to both these places to find out how they work.

SCRIPT THE CRITICAL MOVES

Much like the elephant, who gets spooked by too much change, the rider can get confused or forgetful if we try to explain everything in laborious detail. Changes tend to hang together in bunches, so that once you've done one thing, other things naturally follow. The trick therefore is to reduce your challenge to a few simple ideas that the rider can remember.

All healthcare professionals are required to regularly attend Basic Life Support training (BLS). This has the simplest of algorithms, ABC: airway, breathing, circulation. We don't need to teach every possible combination of injury or disaster – we don't need a vast spider diagram of decision boxes – we need only to script the critical moves. Clear the airway, support the breathing, and manage the circulation. Many other challenges can be reduced to similarly simple ideas. This can be seen in my previous examples: "just fill in the CDU pro-forma" (and the patient's suitability will thereby be assessed), "just use the WHO checklist" (and surgical errors will be reduced), "record the observations on all newborn babies" (and you'll catch the ones that are sick). Less can be more.

POINT TO THE DESTINATION

In this last of the three ways to garner commitment from the rider we come to the place where most leaders are tempted to start. At some point we need to explain what success looks like, preferably in numbers, or in ways that are otherwise unambiguous. Success only really feels like success if we can demonstrate it using numbers. A certificate or commendation may provide us with something tangible, but in the context of continuous performance, we need a measure against which we can compare our level of attainment. In other words, we need a target.

Targets are a mixed blessing. Targets, if used badly, can provide a context-free stick with which to beat an already weary workforce. Their capacity to do the latter has put them in bad odour within healthcare – not least in my own speciality, where the notorious "four-hour-wait" has sapped the goodwill of many emergency department workers.[46] However, they also provide a level of clarity that, in the context of a commitment gained in the ways outlined above, can itself be powerfully motivating

To make a target work well, you will need to find a clear measure that is relevant and motivating and that also demonstrates clearly to your colleagues what success will look like. The next section describes how you can do that.

IMAGINE SUCCESS

Having talked about motivation, I'd like now to cover the more concrete aspect of commitment in more detail. This builds on the idea of pointing to the destination by making clear what your measure of success will be.

To illustrate the point, let me tell you about some work I did recently with a colleague called Vanessa, a very experienced theatre manager, who was having problems with accountable items. These are the small pieces of equipment used in operating theatres that are easily lost: scalpels, clamps, needles, swabs and so forth (the small items you might readily leave inside a patient). She was worried about how committed her staff were to accounting for these items correctly every single time an operation took place. She had already done a lot of work with these individuals on the importance of the scrub-nurse role in protecting the patient ("grow your people") and reminded them all of how catastrophic any retained instruments would be ("find the feeling"); she had done some training and created a Standard Operating Procedure ("script the critical moves"); and she'd made it clear that she needed 100 per cent compliance ("point to the destination"). So far, so good.

The question was, however, how to measure this. Her immediate response was: "We'll audit it". If you've worked in healthcare for long enough, you'll realise that "We'll audit it" is a standard response. My challenge to her was that an occasional audit – someone looking over the shoulder every now and then – would not provide the true assurance that this was being done 100 per cent of the time. You couldn't detect, say, the one in a hundred or even one in a thousand times that it was not being done correctly. The loss of an accountable item – a retained swab for instance – was too important. Ninety-nine point nine per cent wasn't good enough. In this case it had to be 100 per cent. No compromise.

Measuring this may sound tricky, but we discussed it and came up with a solution that has worked a treat. We revamped the countable items sheet that she was using in theatre and added a tear-off slip to the bottom. The sheet was already used to calculate and then re-check the total number of items used and the new tear-off sheet at the bottom was part of the reconciliation. All we changed was that this slip was signed by the scrub-nurse and put in a box near Vanessa's office. You might think that this would add considerably to the workload, but in fact the count-sheet is already part of the system and the process of signing, tearing off and filing took no more than a few seconds. When analysing the tear-off slips, all she was interested in was whether it had the reconciliation number (any number would do, we weren't about to re-check) along with a signature. This was, she reckoned, a sufficiently good indicator that the countable items sheet was being used correctly and this in turn was a sufficient proxy for the process of checking and re-checking that was required. All we needed to do was count the number of operations and count the number of correctly signed slips.

It's true that this system could be gamed by scrub-nurses simply faking the counting process and providing inaccurate or made up slips. Our view was that such misrepresentation was highly unlikely, given the professionalism of the staff involved, and would probably be caught pretty quickly. What we wanted was a simple measure that gave us assurance that the counting process was being conducted correctly every time. The tear-off slips gave us this very quickly as a simple ratio: number of correct slips as a proportion of the number of operations. Target: 100 per cent.

I tell this story in some detail because it highlights an important point that is often missed in healthcare, namely the distinction between audit and continuous improvement. Audit only measures intermittently and is therefore the poor relation of continuous measurement. Other high-risk industries don't rely on audit. You wouldn't want the quality of your domestic water supply to be monitored just once a quarter. Aircraft manufacturers don't just make it and hope: they eliminate error by testing every item they make. In healthcare, until clinical data-collection systems improve markedly, we will need to rely on audit to monitor standards of interventions that are themselves infrequent. But for many of the challenges that I have discussed with healthcare leaders, audit is not a sensible approach. We need instead, like Vanessa, to find simple systems of measurement that give us assurance in real time. We will return to this in the Uniform chapter.

The next exercise is arguably the most important in this entire book. In this, we need to turn all our qualitative descriptions into something that is entirely quantitative – preferably without resorting to audit.

EXERCISE 8: DRAW A GRAPH

Return to your leadership challenge, and to the final question in Exercise 7. Decide on your critical measure of success.

- Now draw a graph with two axes:
- Place a dot in the top right hand corner of your graph. This is your target.
- Label your vertical axis with your measure of success, with an appropriate figure in line with your target. Place another dot on the vertical axis at the level you are currently achieving (or where you think you are performing). This is your base.
- Label the horizontal axis as showing time, with appropriate divisions. e.g. if you think it will take three months to achieve your target, divide into three months. If you think it will take four years, divide into years.
- Now draw a graph between your base and your target in a shape that seems realistic. If you think success will come early, draw your line up and then flatten out. If you think success will come late, draw a line which rises towards the end. If you think progress will be steady, draw a straight line between the two.
- Absolute accuracy is not a prerequisite for this exercise. A rough shape will suffice.

Many people find this exercise remarkably difficult. I would urge you not to skimp or gloss over this difficulty. Without numbers, your project will become – in a memorable phrase – "all smoke and mirrors". Deciding what to measure may in fact require a degree of imagination because it is very likely that you do not measure this variable at the moment (if you did, you would probably have a handle on the problem). Or the measure may not be easily available, or may be inaccurate or not measured frequently enough. It's likely you will be forced to implement some new process steps, like Vanessa, in order to get your new measure in place.

Remember that the measure is for the rider, not the elephant. You can choose a softer measure, like patient or staff opinions, or you can chose something more financial or operational such as "worked hours per unit of service". Just because the elephant won't directly connect with the latter is no reason not to choose it. What is important is that the link between the measure and the emotional commitment is clear. If the elephant is concerned with patient care, then you must provide a convincing case that efficiency gains are in the interests of patients.

Finally, you will need to know that you can collect data for this measure frequently enough, and easily enough, to keep track of progress.

If you find this exercise a struggle, get help from your colleagues. Do not despair. And do not skip over the exercise. The visualisation you are trying to create will engender a degree of planning and foresight as well as commitment. Please take your time, until you can clearly imagine your success as a graph.

With this graph, you are in a strong position to recruit other people to your cause. For this, you may find some use for the ideas presented in the next section.

SHARPEN YOUR WEAPONS OF INFLUENCE

This example may have happened to you at work. You ring up a colleague in another department and suggest something that needs to happen. You are rebuffed. You mention it to your boss. Your boss has a word with the boss of the other department. And now it happens. You suggestion is accepted and all is well. Except that it's not. You are left with a distasteful feeling about why you couldn't persuade your colleague in the first place. This experience is common for a doctor in training trying to refer a patient from one speciality to another and it's common in other walks of life.

So, before you rush off with your leadership challenge and start trying to garner commitment from your colleagues, it's worth stopping for a moment and asking how successful you're likely to be. If you have doubts, that's good. The road to persuasion is littered with brilliant ideas long abandoned.

CIALDINI'S SIX PRINCIPLES

The person to turn to for guidance is another American professor of psychology, this time from Arizona State University, who has been studying persuasion and influence for many decades. His name is Robert Cialdini (I mentioned him before when talking about "being wrong"). His research into the advertising industry is brilliantly and amusingly detailed in his book *Influence*.[47]

He suggests his six principles of influence result from shortcuts in our own behaviour, shortcuts we need to survive in a complex society. These, he says, are hijacked by the advertising industry and used as weapons against us. By understanding them you can turn them to your own advantage. Here I offer a very brief outline of these six ideas.

Reciprocity

If you do something for someone, they will do something for you. You are more likely to buy a magazine from a vendor lurking outside a supermarket if he opens the door for you. You are more likely to donate to a charity if they include a pen in their mailshot. If someone sends you a seasonal card, you're more likely to send them one back. More insidiously, you are more likely to prescribe a drug if the company that makes it has given you lunch. Thankfully, standardisation in the NHS makes this a less common effect than in other health systems.

This need for reciprocity is derived from a primitive instinct towards indebtedness, the presence of which has improved the evolutionary life chances of human groups. Reciprocity is embedded deep within our genes.

What it means for you is that you will get more support for your leadership challenge if you can help someone else with their problems. If you scratch their back, they are likely to view your suggestions favourably. Failing that, a simple gesture or gift will put them on your side. Thank-you letters, described in detail in the Introduction, do this very effectively.

Commitment and consistency

As I mentioned in the Introduction, once someone has agreed or disagreed with something, it's much more difficult for them to change their mind. People will agree with something, or support something, if they think that a decision fits with previous decisions, or with their self-image.

What this means for you is two things. First, don't allow people to say "no" too early. If you force people to consider your leadership challenge too early and take a judgment, you run the risk that they will decide against you – and that means you'll have much more work to do to persuade them otherwise.

Second, remember that self-identity is an important part of making a decision. If you can present your leadership challenge as being consistent with someone's current position, you'll have more success. For instance, if you emphasise that your leadership challenge is good for patient safety, it will likely find favour with clinicians. If it also saves money, you can emphasise this when pitching to the finance manager.

Social proof

This one is straightforward. We do things that other people are doing. Clothing fashions are an obvious manifestation of this. But there are fashions in healthcare too, despite our best efforts to make all medicine evidence-based. If we think that "people like us" believe something, then we will be much more likely to agree. Advertisers use "people like us" in their adverts for a reason (although, as we shall see, they usually use models).

What this means – and you'll know this already – is that success breeds success in persuasion. If you can convince one person, their support alone will win over others. Choose your first conversations wisely, since you'll be building on them to get your leadership challenge accepted.

It also means that if you can find examples elsewhere – either as bright spots or, perhaps, as research – then you'll be better able to persuade others.

Authority

This explains the story that heads this section. If your boss tells you, then well … you do it. It's true that if a leader does nothing but tell people, their authority will be eroded, as I've discussed already in the Introduction. But if you want something done quickly, authority is the quickest route. People will, on the whole, submit to authority – even if they strongly disagree with what they are doing. The famous Milgram experiments, where subjects were persuaded to electrocute strangers at the behest of white-coated "researchers", showed that without doubt.[48]

The disadvantage is that authority can persuade without creating commitment, so I would caution against using authority when trying to garner support, since it can quickly unravel.

Liking

The fifth of Cialdini's factors is something we would perhaps prefer not to acknowledge. We are more likely to agree with someone and to do what they say if we like them. This includes being attracted to them, which explains why almost all adverts are presented with models rather than real people.

You probably won't be able to employ a supermodel to help you with your leadership challenge, but that doesn't mean that liking is unimportant. In fact, in some cases it may possible be the most important of all these factors. If people don't like you they will be more reluctant to support you, even if that reluctance is subconscious.

There are many ways to make yourself likeable – sprucing yourself up and smiling being the simplest – but being positive is by far the most important. As described in the Introduction, your overall attitude and language, your visibility, saying thank you, talking up – striving for the 5:1 ratio – are all ways to become more likeable.

Machiavelli, the iconic political theorist of 16th century Florence, famously asked his prince whether it is better to be loved than feared or feared than loved? His answer was "One should wish to be both, but, because it is difficult to unite them in one person, it is much safer to be feared than loved". The corollary of this is, of course, that if you can't be feared (which in modern working environment would be disastrous) then you must be loved. In other words: "If you're not the boss, make sure that people like you."

Scarcity

The last of Cialdini's weapons of influence is scarcity. People will act differently if they think there's a shortage. Panic buying is only one example. Auction houses, including those online, make trillions of dollars out of this principle; as an auction ends, potential buyers stare scarcity in the face, and bid beyond what they would have done without the pressure of the clock. It is an extraordinarily powerful emotion, as anyone who has bid competitively online will know.

This may suggest that if you can couch your leadership challenge in terms of scarcity, then you will be in a better position to win commitment from others. It may, but once again I would urge caution. We are all suspicious that signs saying "last weekend of sale" really mean "last weekend until the next one". Similarly, recruitment drives couched as a war for talent may not really convince. Scarcity is testable and must therefore be real. If you can prove scarcity, you will have less trouble garnering commitment.

LEARN THE LANGUAGE OF COMMITMENT

Before we close this chapter on commitment, there are two final pieces of the jigsaw that may help you. One is about language, the other about meetings.

A year or so before writing this book, I was working on an IT project. When we started the development phase, we quickly discovered that our chief developer had a number of stock phrases: "I'll see what I can do", "I'm hopeful I can manage that" and "I'll try to get that done" are just a selection. This vagueness resulted in a slew of missed deadlines and a total lack of progress. It turned out that he couldn't deliver on his promises. In fact, looking back, I realise that he didn't make any promises.

Given the importance of language it's worth considering how you gauge the commitment of others through their language and how you demonstrate your own commitment. There are some phrases – such as those above – that are clear pointers to a lack of commitment, others that are perhaps more subtle. A favourite is "I'll get back to you" (always assume they won't). Words of commitment include: will, definitely, today, certainly, immediately. Lack of commitment seeps through with words like: might, sometime, maybe, soon, perhaps and, worst of all, try. As Yoda advised: "Do or do not. There is no try."

My suggestion – as emphasised in the Introduction – is to make extensive use of enquiry ("So how do you feel about …?") and acknowledgement ("So you are suggesting that … ?") rather than assertion ("We ought to do …"). Remember that under pressure people can fake commitment, so you need to seek out and unearth other people's level of commitment through enquiry, rather than putting them on the spot. We will discuss this in more detail under the Missing Conversations model on page 144.

For your part, use words of commitment whenever possible. Be certain, be firm, positive and clear. It will help your case.

PRACTISE PRE-PRESENTATION

The final consideration in this chapter is a very practical one. As I mentioned in the introduction, I spent several years as a management consultant. My first project was with a company that manufactured plastic widgets for the car industry. I was part of a team that spent a week going around bothering members of the accounting team and other managers for useful bits of data. We then collated all this into a data pack with which we could make a business case and form a plan to improve productivity by reducing waste. Soon, we had an outline presentation of our findings and recommendations. "Right", said the project leader, "time for some pre-presents."

Let me translate. Our job at the end of the week was to hold a "qualification meeting" to persuade the management team that our plan was brilliant and that they needed to employ us to help them implement it. This qualification meeting was a big show where we presented our findings and encouraged them all to agree how big and how complicated this improvement project would be. Try to imagine that we simply kept this data pack and project plan to ourselves and then, ta–da, revealed this to 20 executives all at once. The effect, you may imagine, would be a cacophony of disapproval, challenges and mayhem. As one of my colleagues once said: "If you do that they'll trash the numbers, trash the process and trash the people. Usually in that order."

The better alternative was to seek out every member of the meeting individually and sit down with them and go through the pack in detail, one-to-one. These pre-presentation meetings – or pre-presents – gave each attendee a chance to understand the data and any proposals, to raise any objections, and for us to correct any errors. The result is that the set-piece meeting then had no surprises. No chimps' cages were rattled, no elephants were spooked and no one got hot under the collar. As a result, everyone could make a joint decision as if it was the easiest thing in the world.

I commend this pre-present process to anyone trying to get broad agreement from a group – especially a senior, busy or poorly aligned group – when you have a leadership challenge that is going to require a change in attitudes, some re-alignment, or some re-negotiation. Don't attempt to make such decisions in a meeting of more than three people. Go to everyone involved, talk it through, get overall agreement to the idea and only then bring it up in a group meeting for formal sign-off.

At that point, once commitment and agreement have been achieved, you are ready for action. And it is action which is the subject of the next chapter.

ACTIVE
Manage the workload

A little less conversation, a little more action.

– ELVIS PRESLEY [49]

Not long ago I spent a few months coaching a group of senior hospital managers. They had significant problems as a group. The performance of their various clinical units was, to be frank, dire. The enormous increase in pressure from patients arriving into the Emergency Department meant that they had to find space in the hospital every hour of every day where none existed. Doing this safely was difficult. Patients were being moved into temporary wards in community hospitals, into beds designed for day-stay (endoscopy and the like). And every month, the problem was getting worse. The numbers arriving through the front door kept growing, even through the summer. Despite opening new wards and trying every trick in the book, there was no relief. On top of this, they were being asked to make huge cost savings and efficiency gains. Everyone was buckling under the pressure and many permanent staff were leaving. Agency costs were rising and recruitment was proving difficult. In short, the hospital was in a constant state of near collapse.

As pressure built during each day, the managers spent much of their time in emergency planning meetings chaired by their chief operating officer. The hospital was pitched at various levels of escalation – a euphemism for crisis – ranging from green, yellow, amber, red and then black. Black was the most common state of affairs. The planning meetings, which were mostly undocumented, allowed the senior managers to coordinate and agree on more drastic measures to free space within the hospital.

The impact on the morale of the senior leaders themselves and their staff was catastrophic. And this situation meant that the hospital was missing almost all of its performance targets. One surgeon had failed to operate on any elective patient for nearly a year because all his beds had been taken over by emergency medical patients. He was suing his employer for allowing his skills to atrophy.

Apart from the obvious complaint that the wider system was broken, the main concern of the leaders I worked with was that they couldn't get anything done. They spent so much time in meetings that they had little time for anything else; they had no to think through or execute any higher strategy. They spent much of their meetings in "Crackberry mode", responding (usually under the table, but visible) to their hundreds of daily email messages. In short, they were on fire – but not in a good way.

If you're a healthcare leader, you will may not be surprised to hear that the situation facing these individuals is not uncommon. You may even face similar situations yourself. Much of the UK health system is buckling under pressure from rising demand and the ineffectiveness of central planning. From my experience in other countries, the UK is not alone. Even in the USA, where health spending is so much higher, many hospitals are in a similar state. I said in the introduction to this book that healthcare leadership is hard. It is.

You will not be surprised to hear that the hospital's problems extended beyond anything I could influence as an outsider, especially as the HR department, who had pitched my coaching sessions as a personal development exercise, limited my intervention to a few short meetings. All I could hope to do was help them find a way to focus, prioritise and thereby create some space in which to think. Much of what we discussed is presented in this chapter.

TIME AND ACTION MANAGEMENT

The two main themes in this chapter are time management – or, more accurately, action management – and meeting effectiveness. I will first discuss an approach to developing your own action-management system. I will then touch on the distinction between planning activities and planning for results. Then, after a brief discussion about gathering a team around you, we will deal with the thorny subject of meetings – and in particular how to successfully prepare and manage decision-making meetings.

Let us start by examining how we manage our time.

EXPAND THE GOLDEN QUADRANT

The 34th president of the USA, Dwight D Eisenhower, said:

I have two kinds of problems, the urgent and the important. The urgent are not important, and the important are never urgent.[50]

Since then, he has been credited with inventing what is now called the Eisenhower principle of time management. In this, tasks are divided into four types (see diagram below).

FIGURE 1: Urgency *vs* importance

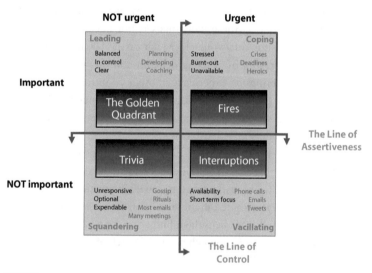

FIRES

In the top right quadrant are tasks that are both urgent and important. I call these Fires because they must be attended to *and* they must be attended to *now*. Because crises tend to feed off each other, fires tend to spread.

The leaders I described above were deep in this quadrant. Almost all of their time was spent dealing with crises, leaving very little time for anything else and the effect on them, like anyone else spending too much time in this quadrant, was clear: stress, burnout and unavailability.

Leaders whose time predominates in this quadrant are coping rather than leading.

INTERRUPTIONS

Tasks that are urgent but not important consume time without achieving much: emails that need to be read, some phone calls, "can I have a moment" conversations, Interruptions. Time spent on these tasks makes leaders available, which may be important to those who want some of their time, but places them in a position of short-term focus, which may be bad news for longer-term planning.

Leaders who spend their time here are vacillating.

TRIVIA

Tasks that are neither important nor urgent I call Trivia: gossiping, indulging in various rituals, aimless internet surfing or perfecting things (a personal favourite of mine is font-hunting). Many of the emails we deal with are trivial, simply because they are not important – at least not to us – and they are not urgent. Ditto some of the terrible meetings that we are forced to attend.

Any time spent here is squandered.

THE GOLDEN QUADRANT

Finally, those tasks that are important but not urgent fit into what I call the Golden Quadrant. Almost all of the tasks of leadership – many of which will be discussed in this and later chapters – are here: coaching, planning, motivating, training, reporting, researching, networking, developing, forecasting, communicating … this is where we should spend most of our time as leaders, but so seldom do. Leaders who spend time predominantly in this quadrant are, indeed, leading. That's the point.

It is my assertion that great leaders, and Eisenhower was no doubt one of them, spend as much time as feasible in the Golden Quadrant. Think back to your favourite leader from the exercise in the introduction. Were the qualities that they exhibited, which you admired, founded upon time spent in the Golden Quadrant? I would bet they were. It is unlikely you remember them for their capacity to squander their time, vacillate or merely cope with situations.

EXERCISE 9: WHERE DO YOU SPEND YOUR TIME?

Think about your last week at work. If necessary, return to your diary. Think of each hour at work and ask yourself in which of the four quadrants you found yourself. Total up each quadrant and give yourself a rough percentage for each quadrant.

If your work has a large clinical component, you will need to consider whether "patient–facing" time should be considered urgent, important, neither or both. The temptation is to say that it is both urgent and important and therefore comes under "fires". However, rather than lump this all together, my suggestion is to look carefully at the detail within each activity and divide your time even further. If you're in a clinic, on the shop floor or in a ward round, how much time is spent searching for things, waiting for people or dealing with irritations, rather than making clinical decisions or teaching? If you have a four-hour ward round, for instance, how much of that is spent in "golden quadrant moments", talking to patients and staff, making high quality decisions or developing your colleagues. How much, by contrast, is used up dealing with interruptions, gossip or crises?

Add up your totals and give yourself a percentage for each quadrant.

Many healthcare leaders I speak to reveal that they spend more than 70 per cent of their time dealing with fires and interruptions and less than ten per cent of their time in the Golden Quadrant. They want to do more of the leadership activity, but are stymied by the unexpected. If this is the case for you, don't despair. Study the diagram again and you'll notice two grey lines, which represent two suggestions that may help you.

SHIFT THE LINE OF ASSERTIVENESS

Time at work is finite – it can be stretched by working longer hours or taking your work home, but that's not really helpful since it merely increases your levels of stress and unhappiness and makes you less productive in the long run. Within a finite time you must therefore find a way to *increase* the amount of time available for Golden Quadrant activities – i.e. you have to shift work *into* the Golden Quadrant by shovelling work *out* of the other quadrants. By definition you can't remove the fires: they must be attended to, and attended to *now*. This means that you have to shift time out of the bottom two quadrants. You have to shift the line of assertiveness down.

The line of assertiveness is best described as your capacity to say "No!" to the activities in the two lower quadrants. This principally means ignoring or fending off interruptions. Having an open door policy is great, but you'll be plagued by people traipsing through it. Give yourself uninterrupted time – yes, you can go home, to the library or even to your car – but only if you do the Golden Quadrant work. Turn off your email. Leave your phone at your desk. Make yourself unavailable.

Remember: if there really is a fire, they'll come and get you – or they'll find another fire-fighter.

Saying No can actually give you huge chunks of time if you are suitably assertive: saying No to being on a committee; saying No to re-writing a report; saying No to doing the report in the first place (what's wrong with a summary email); saying No to people who just want a word (you can offer them a scheduled meeting). There is a lot of time out there that you can grab by just saying No.

You may need to choose your moments, but time will only come to you when you are assertive enough to say No. I know one leader who has an automatic response on his email system that says "I do not read emails on which I am cc'd".

You will also need to find some self-control to avoid the trivia. Simply ignoring many of your emails and phone calls may help. But you may also need to stop yourself doing things that you pretend are important, but are in fact time-wasters. Time disappears into internet "research", font hunting, and conversations by the water cooler. I'm not suggesting you never chat idly to your colleagues – there is an essential social dimension to both work and leadership – but you may need to assess the amount of time you dedicate to this.

SHIFT THE LINE OF CONTROL

Having wrestled a bit of time out of the lower quadrants, you must now use it for fire prevention, not for further fire-fighting. That means using your new assertiveness-delivered time for golden quadrant activity, not dealing with yet another crisis. You need to spend time developing your staff, planning for the future, learning from the past. You mustn't just go back onto the shop floor and make yourself available for urgent matters. The reason for this is clear: the only thing that will stop crises from happening in the future is *better leadership* – i.e. more Golden Quadrant activity. In other words, your leadership needs to improve in order to stop the fires from breaking out around you.

Shifting the line of control is, to a large extent, what this entire book is about. Developing and employing the skills that are described in these chapters are precisely the activities that will create the systems, the processes and the behaviour for you to deliver safe, caring and effective service. It will also improve the response when a fire does break out.

So, let us assume that you've wrestled a few moments from your day by saying NO in a clear but assertive manner. All is quiet. You have forged some space. It is at this point the question arises: what do you do now?

TAKE CONTROL OF YOUR ACTIONS

I once had a colleague who carried around a clip-board with his to-do list on it. Every time he completed an action, he would purposefully strike out the item on his list using a motion that was deep and deliberate and – if the action had been persistent or difficult – repeated several times. He looked at me once, having just crossed out some irksome task and smiled wistfully. "I just love completing my actions" he said.

I'm not suggesting that he was entirely normal, and I have to agree that it may be futile to invest yourself too heavily in crossing things off your to-do list, but I think he had a point: there is satisfaction to be gained from doing so. The obverse of this truth is perhaps more significant: there is a great deal of dissatisfaction in *failing* to get things done, whether that is as an individual, a team or a wider organisation. And that satisfaction eludes you for only two reasons: either you don't have a to-do list or you find difficulty in completing your actions. After reading the Commitment chapter, you may have developed the unwavering resolve to achieve wonders, but if you can't get things done then (to quote one of my good friends) you can't implement a toffee.

As a leader, there are therefore two skills you need to acquire if you want to turn ambition into reality, and if you want to make good use of your Golden Quadrant time. One is the personal skill of what used to be called time management, but is perhaps more correctly considered action management – i.e. making sure that you do the things that you need to do in the right order, as efficiently and as effectively as possible. The second equally important skill is making sure that your colleagues do the same.

To give you an idea of why action management – rather than time management – is the phrase I use, let me give you a brief description of this, the very day that I wrote this chapter: my diary is clear of meetings. This is a day set aside for writing. The only thing on my to-do list is "Write Active Chapter". I get up early. I can write an entire chapter of this book if undisturbed. I begin by ensuring my emails – which have piled up after a couple of clinical days on-call – are dealt with. A few issues arise from that. I deal with them. The doorbell rings. I have a discussion with the guy who has come to paint my house. As a result, I have to make some more calls. I return to my desk. I empty my physical inbox of items – ensuring that there is nothing I need to do urgently. Some more emails come in – and I field most of them but one requires me to reformat an article I've written. It takes longer than I thought. I then remember there is one important thing I wanted to research on the internet … I look up. It's already lunchtime. I have a snack. My family returns and I spend some time talking to them. My snack turns into a lunch-hour. The doorbell rings again. It's a collection I'd forgotten about. It takes me a while to sort that out. Finally … it's nearly three o'clock in the afternoon and I've not written a word.

You will probably conclude from this little vignette that I don't follow my own advice and that I'm totally unfocused. Despite working alone, I have allowed myself to be distracted by trivia and interruptions galore. However, all is not lost – because you are reading the fruits of that day, albeit a disappointingly smaller proportion of the day than I had hoped. When the space eventually opened up, *I knew exactly what I needed to do*.

For all leaders, clinical or otherwise, the situation at work is much more complex and much more fluid than sitting at home writing, although the contrast between the important and the urgent is no more stark. Against a background of ongoing crises, there is an avalanche of emails, phone calls and other interruptions. Once you find that lacuna of peace, you must be ready for the *right* action, given the time available and the priorities you have. This means you have to have an action-management system that is flexible enough to withstand the fluid nature of your work environment. It is for this reason that rigid time planning systems are largely out of favour. No fixed time set aside for Golden Quadrant activity will survive the fire caused by patient numbers running out of control or several staff members failing to turn up for work. Diarising your actions will almost inevitably lead to disappointment.

The solution is to have an action management system. What follows is a description of my own approach.

CHOOSE YOUR SYSTEM

The way I manage my own action list is inspired by the work of David Allen, whose books and philosophy of "Getting Things Done" (GTD) [51] have spawned a small industry in helping leaders manage their increasingly complex lives. You may find that another system works for you, but bear in mind that whatever you use must be simple enough to manage moment-to-moment and flexible enough to work around the interruptions that will inevitably arise.

At it's core, the GTD system recommends that you write down *every* action that you may need to remember. This prevents you from having to remember them on the fly. Merely trying to recall what's next and what's important is a huge time-waster (because you're bound to forget something) and causes anxiety even when you don't need to remember things (because you worry that you might forget). For instance, if when you go past a colleague's desk, or open a cluttered cupboard you think, "Oooh, I must remember to …" you are using energy created by an open loop in your mind. Writing it down in a reliable system closes that loop and allows your mind to relax. The action is captured even if it's not completed. It creates the reassurance that "Although I'm not actually doing it, at least I'm not forgetting it". With a closed system, replete with *all* your actions, you no longer have to remember to remember, thus relieving your mental faculties of a huge burden.

COLLECT AND COLLATE

So, in the GTD philosophy, you capture *everything* you know you must, or feel you might need to, remember. Yes, *everything*. That includes everything in your domestic situation or other aspects of your life. If you don't already have a comprehensive list dedicate a day to making one. Your task is to make a complete list, possibly an enormous list, of every single action, great or small, that you may need to remember. This includes every email, note or report you need to write, every conversation, or phone call you need to make. You need to capture each memo, sticky-note and passing thought that you might ever have to recall. Gather this all into one place.

Now group the actions into projects. A project in this case is any collection of actions to achieve a task. From clearing out the garage to introducing a new set of clinical guidelines; from researching and buying a new road bike to re-negotiating your terms and conditions of employment. For each project write down two thing. First, write down the goal. What does success look like? When will you be able to say something is finished? Second, ensure that you have written down the first few actions that you can think of. Don't try to plan the whole thing. Just work out what comes next and make sure that all of your actions are sorted into these projects.

Finally, divide your various projects into your areas of responsibility. At work that may include your various roles: governance lead, service manager, clinical officer, for instance. And at home – or further afield – you may have: family, charity, music, sport, creative. It's up to you. For each area of responsibility you should clarify one or two goals (these will probably include your commitments from the previous chapter). Finally, you need to sort each of your actions into: do next, scheduled for a particular date and some day in the future.

At the time of writing, I personally have six areas of responsibility, 18 active projects and about 250 actions on my to-do list, many of which are scheduled for the future or are in "someday". This leaves about 30 to 40 currently active items that need to be done next. A few of these are marked to be done today.

The key to the GTD philosophy is then keeping this list up to date and relevant by doing two things regularly: processing and reviewing.

MAINTAIN AND PROCESS

You need to keep this to-do list up to date by adopting two habits. First, you must write down every single action as soon as it comes to you (unless you're actually going to do it right there and then). Don't assume you'll remember it. Even if you do remember, the effort of doing so will sap you of mental energy. I write down every action that comes to me in every meeting, in every conversation. Everything from buying new bike lights to preparing for exams. They all go on the list.

The second habit you'll need to develop is frequently processing what comes to you, both physically and online. This means, at least once per day, working sequentially through your accumulated emails, letters, and other physical reminders (which you should store together in a single in-tray or box). For each item, you have to choose one of three outcomes: 1) if it will take less than two minutes, deal with it immediately – respond, purchase, phone – whatever it takes; 2) if it will take longer than two minutes, put a new action on your to-do list; 3) if it doesn't need an action, but you need to keep it, file the object or record somewhere in a storage system so you can find it when you need it. You can use this processing time to make fine adjustments to your to-do list, ensuring that all your actions are available for review.

REVIEW AND PRIORITISE

Finally, you need to review your list, your projects and your goals. David Allen recommends doing different sorts of reviews at different frequencies: a weekly sort out, a monthly overview and a yearly or half-yearly 10,000 metre view, asking yourself if you're on track to complete your goals, and whether you're concentrating overall on the right things. You should do a quick daily review every time you process your inbox.

Such a concise summary cannot do full justice to the GTD system. There are many books on the subject, and there are countless tools, paper-based, offline and online that can be used to complement it. All I can say is that it has worked for me and countless other people, so I can only really recommend that you research it – and compare it with any other system that you think might work for you.

Whatever system you settle on, I would urge you to ensure that it gives you real clarity of your actions, their relationships to your goals and their priorities. The aim is to have something really simple yet flexible and clear enough that when a sudden period of Golden Quadrant time opens up, you will know with certainty what to do next, confident that you're not missing or forgetting something.

At least, that is, until the next interruption.

PLAN FOR RESULTS, NOT ACTIVITIES

Having now sorted out your own action list, I want to digress slightly into a subject which I hope will make you more effective in managing and delivering projects, such as your leadership challenge.

What I have found is that the principles of action management are applied to projects to the exclusion of results management – i.e. projects are planned with a focus on actions and activities without first agreeing to a measurable deliverable, a result. The managers who I mentioned at the beginning of this chapter were very action focused but they had not seen any data. They were not planning for results, mainly because it's a Golden Quadrant activity.

In my experience, it is not uncommon to plan and plan and plan and to keep on planning until every possible activity has been considered – producing an enormous action plan. Unfortunately, we usually discover the truth of the adage "No action plan survives contact with the enemy".[52]

If found to be inadequate for some reason, the action plan is re-worked. The problem is, we never know enough about the future to make an action plan that will not need to be re-written.

Instead of this, we need first commit to a destination – to a measurable result – just as we have in the Committed chapter. This is what is called, in military circles, the commander's intent, a way of providing a clear ambition without needing to plan every step of the way. Once we have that, we can plan the top-level changes that will deliver the result. Once we have agreed overall changes, we can then decide the first few detailed actions or activities which will make a start on these changes. It is counter-productive to plan too far ahead or in too much detail. I can't emphasise this point strongly enough: plan for results and only then agree what the *next* actions are.

For more complicated projects, it may be easier to split your result into parts and then plan for these interconnected results, rather than attack a single overall result in one chunk. Let me offer an example. Imagine that the result you want is an improvement in theatre utilisation from 60 per cent (your base) to 80 per cent (your target) over a year. You may have identified several factors that contribute to this, such as late starts, cancelled operations, intra-operative delays and staff unavailability. Each of these factors will need a base and a target, which together contribute to the overall result. These individual results then become the focus of your results-planning efforts. You might, for instance, aim to reduce the percentage of late-starting operations from 30 per cent to 10 per cent. To do so, you may decide that one of the changes will be to provide theatre-lists to the wards the night before. This single change may require many actions, but the first action is likely to involve discussing this change with the theatre and managers. That's all you need to do next. That's probably all we need to capture, initially. The action may seem small, but it is powerful because it is couched in the context of achieving an overall result.

Planning for results, rather than activities may seem just a syntactic change, but it's not trivial. It makes a huge difference, as we shall see when we talk about Management Reports later in this chapter. Your meetings and communication will become much more effective if they are focused on the numbers. In summary, I would urge you to spend much more time defining your results rather than the activities that may flow from them.

EXERCISE 11: PLAN YOUR RESULT

From Exercise 8: Draw a Graph, you should now have a graph showing a base and a target and some planned performance over time for your leadership challenge. The next step is to create an outline project plan.

1.   Consider whether your result can easily be split into contributory factors – sub-results that will themselves add up to the result you want. If so, you should create a series of sub-graphs which together demonstrate how your results are derived.

2.   For each graph decide on which overall activities or changes will deliver these results.

3.   For each activity or overall change decide on the first few actions that you will need to pursue in order to deliver that change.

GATHER YOUR TEAM

We now come to the second, more difficult, skill required of any leader when it comes to getting things done, namely getting things done through other people. To achieve the goals of any leadership challenge, you will need to gather and motivate a team of people to pursue this challenge with you.

This may, of course, be the group of people that you already manage directly, in which case the complexity of drawing these people together is much reduced. If, on the other hand, you need to engage a more disparate group – a situation which is, in my experience, much more likely – then you will need to use the suggestions from the Committed chapter to garner their support.

Even if your leadership challenge requires you to engage your own direct reports, don't assume that you can rely on their commitment. Whomever you wish to engage as part of a team, I strongly suggest that you pre-present, one-to-one, the overall aims and results, looking to motivate the elephant before directing the rider while remembering to enquire, acknowledge, then advocate.

Through this process, you should gather a group of people who want to help you deliver. This is your Delivery Team.[53] You need the team to be big enough, so that it won't falter when you are absent, and so big that it's difficult to manage. I would recommend between six and ten people.

> **EXERCISE 12: GATHER YOUR TEAM**
>
> Identify six to ten individuals who you would like to help you with your leadership challenge. Visit them all individually and discuss the challenge, your result and your results plan.
>
> Remember to listen hard: enquire, acknowledge, and then advocate. Look for opportunities to motivate the elephant before directing the rider.
>
> Test their commitment by asking them to attend regular meetings with other members of your delivery team.

The job of this team is to manage the actions that are needed to deliver the result, as we shall discuss in the next section. You therefore then need to ensure that each of the people in this group has a suitable action management system, as described earlier in this chapter. If they don't have such a system you should help them develop one. My strong suggestion is that you use an online tool to share actions for the project during your meetings.[54]

TWO MODELS AND FOUR TOOLS

We all hate meetings. At least, most of us hate most meetings most of the time. We hate them because they are ineffective and boring and useless. In the majority, they take our time and energy away from the Golden Quadrant and burn it. The exceptions are those meetings that are well ordered, where joint decisions are made quickly and effectively, and which contribute something useful to a cause to which we personally feel committed.

You will inevitably find that well-organised meetings which are timely, well chaired and focused on action, are also well attended. Meeting effectiveness attracts people. I would suggest, therefore, that if you're going to get anything done at all, you will need to acquire the skill of designing and running effective decision-making meetings.[57]

Creating and running such meetings is not difficult, but it does require a degree of courage, as well as some thoughtful preparation. To help you, I am going to offer you four useful tools. However, before we discuss these tools in detail, it's worth considering two models that may help you understand why good meetings work well.

THE D-A-D-A MODEL

The first model tries to answer the very general question: what is the overall purpose of having a meeting? In Figure 2, meetings are part of a cycle in which you take Data, Analyse what it is telling you, make some Decisions about Actions which will then, in turn, change the Data (D-A-D-A).[55]

To illustrate this, imagine you are trying to reduce waiting times in an outpatient department. You convene a monthly meeting to discuss this. The Data you bring to the meeting is a list of clinics and their waiting times. You discuss and Analyse the data and perhaps conclude that a problem is that appointments for new patients are causing delays. You Decide to run a trial where clinics schedule all their new patients towards the end, rather than the beginning of the clinic. After the meeting, the participants undertake some actions that put that trial into place. A month later, you bring a new set of Data to the meeting to see what has changed and whether your Actions have had the desired effect. You repeat this cycle of data–analysis–decisions–action until your waiting times have improved to a level with which you are satisfied. In this model, the purpose of meetings is to perform the "Analysis–Decision" part of this cycle.

FIGURE 2: The DADA cycle underpins all sustainable improvement

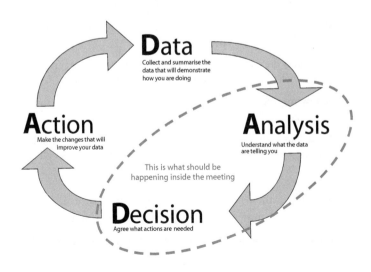

Data
Collect and summarise the data that will demonstrate how you are doing

Analysis
Understand what the data are telling you

This is what should be happening inside the meeting

Decision
Agree what actions are needed

Action
Make the changes that will improve your data

Some people may say that meetings are for communication – i.e. broadcasting information and persuading people of pre-decided facts or policies. You can use meetings for this, but it's an expensive method. Paper and email can do that more efficiently. If all you want to do is tell (i.e. advocate) then I predict you'll not have good attendance. People come to meetings in order to contribute to decisions. If that is not available, they won't come.

KANTOR'S FOUR-PLAYER MODEL

"That DADA model is all very well," you may say. "But this doesn't address the problem of Talking Thomas." Talking Thomas, and his close associates Negative Nancy, Wettie William, and Cynical Simon are attendees who undermine meetings by dominating the conversation, being argumentative, saying nothing or making snide remarks. We all know who they are, and they make meetings unbearable.

The solution is to reframe the problem in a spirit of positivity, away from categorising individuals. Let me offer you a powerful way of thinking about meeting behaviour in terms of what people intend, rather than how they come across.

Below is a brief summary of a model proposed by David Kantor, a clinical psychologist who has been working in the field of family therapy for over four decades.[56] In his "Four-Player" model, he suggests that every intervention that we make in a conversation – i.e. everything we say in a group situation – has one of only four intentions:

Moving generates ideas and provides direction by saying things such as: "Let's do …" or "My idea is …".

Opposing prevents mistakes, corrects and ensures integrity by saying things such as: "That's not quite right …" or "Instead …".

Following offers loyalty, service or completion by saying things such as: "I agree …" or "I'll do that …".

Bystanding moderates and provides perspective or reflection by saying things such as: "We're not on subject …" or "If we just step back …".

Unfortunately, these intentions can be misconstrued, especially if individuals have a propensity for a particular type of intervention:

Movers can be seen as dominating, dictatorial, impatient and over-decisive.

Opposers can be seen as critical, competitive and contrary.

Followers can be seen as indecisive, placating and over-accommodating.

Bystanders can be seen as judgmental, disengaged or withdrawn.

The diagram below summarises this. The Movers and Opposers are on one axis and Bystanders and Followers on the other.

FIGURE 3: Kantor's four-player model of meeting contributions

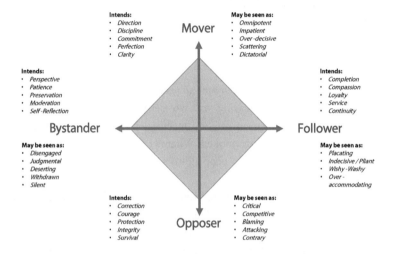

What the model tells us is that for a meeting to be effective we need *all four* of these interventions. We need ideas (movers), which must be challenged and modified (opposers). We need people who will volunteer to take action (followers) and those who will ensure that we don't go off-topic or run out of time (bystanders). To prove the point, just consider what a meeting without one of these contributions might be like: the boredom of a meeting without the ideas provided by movers; the fantasy world of a meeting unchecked by opposers; the fruitlessness of a meeting without followers agreeing to take on work; the unruliness of a meeting without bystanders keeping us to time and on-topic.

This model is relevant to you because, as the person running your meeting, you must balance the contributions made by the participants.

Your job is to encourage the right balance of mover/opposer and follower/bystander. I suggest that you designate yourself as the bystander-in-chief (see "top tips" below) and concentrate on encouraging discussion through the right balance of enquiry, acknowledgement, and advocacy. Each point of discussion should be conducted as a diamond: where the conversation initially fans out by encouraging mover type interventions and then closes down in favour of a decision, using followers and opposers to create consensus. This art of facilitation is discussed in some more detail in the Responsive and Energetic chapters.

FOUR ESSENTIAL TOOLS

I'd like now to describe the four tools that I mentioned earlier, that you will find essential when preparing and running a meeting.[58]

Terms of reference

How many times have you been sent an agenda for a meeting that is simply a list of talking points, leaving you wondering why you've been asked to attend? When preparing for any meeting, you have to ask yourself questions that are often overlooked: What is this meeting *for*? What is the *purpose* of getting a group of people into a room to talk with each other? *Why* are we doing this?

Agreeing on a clear set of objectives makes two things possible: you can ensure the participants are aligned in their reasons for being in the room and you can afterwards judge whether your meeting was successful.

My suggestion is therefore that, for every decision-making meeting, you agree with your participants a meeting terms of reference (TOR), which clarifies all the things that a participant may need.

The one-page meeting TOR should include:

Purpose and objectives: Each of these should start "To ...'

Participants' names or roles, whichever is appropriate.

Date and time, as well as location and frequency.

Inputs – what is brought into the meeting. This should include the data that we are planning to analyse (which should be distributed and read beforehand).

Outputs – what we expect to generate as a result of the meeting (usually a list of actions, but may be more than that).

Ground rules – a list of behaviours which we expect the participants to adhere to: this may include considerations of timeliness, use of mobile phones and bleeps, sending of deputies, etc.

Below is the template that I use.

FIGURE 4: Meeting terms of reference template

Day (s)		Attendees		
Time		•		•
Frequency				
Location				
Purpose/Objectives		**Agenda**		**Time (min)**
• • • •		• Review previous action log • • • • • • Review new action log • Agree meeting effectiveness score		5 5 2
		Total		
Inputs		**Outputs**	**Ground Rules**	
• Previous Action Log • Pre-reads • Management Report		• Updated action log • Meeting Effectiveness Score	• Agree at start of meeting	

My suggestion is that you fill in your own version of this. If there is any likelihood of contention, pre-present it to the participants individually. I mentioned that some courage may be needed. Imagine going to see your colleagues with a new TOR template and saying "This is my plan for next week's meeting, I just want to know if this meets your needs". This may cause them a little surprise, but I can assure you that your meeting will be much more effective if everyone in the room has already agreed on the purpose, outline and ground rules beforehand.

ACTION LOG

We've already mentioned the problem of getting things done through other people. To my mind the action log is the most important tool for this – and it is one in common use, so you will likely have come across them already. In summary, an action log records the decisions and commitments made in a meeting.

Each line of the action log should record:

The issue or project being discussed.

The action. Recording the commitment of the person doing the action. The more precise and outcome-focused, the better.

The person responsible. Just one person, preferably.

The due-date. Agreed to by (not forced on) the person responsible

The status. Just done/not done rather than anything more complex. Traffic-light ratings can encourage prevarication.

My experience is that action logs are rarely used effectively, often because they are used in conjunction with meeting minutes. Personally, I think that minutes should be used only if they are legally necessary, and then should be kept as brief as possible. Let's face it, no one reads them. Action logs are the key to effectiveness. They record the result of discussions and commitments and if the actions are clear and detailed enough, they can substitute for large sections of any minutes. Remember, from the DADA model, that the end-point of any meeting is the decisions that are agreed. The action log can and should capture the results of those conversations.

Top tips for action logs

Here are my top tips for using action logs effectively:

Ensure that the person taking the action dictates the action. The thoughts of the scribe are not the commitment of the speaker. Ask for clarification when someone offers to take an action: "What should we put on the action log?". Make sure they agree on the due date.

Ensure all actions record outcomes not activities. "Call Jim" means nothing. "Gain Jim's agreement to ..." can be tested.

Review the action log *briefly* at the beginning and end of each meeting. Using a projector so that everyone can see and agree the actions is ideal. Do NOT allow the action log review at the beginning to dominate or replace the meeting itself. A simple "Done" or "Not Done" is usually all that is required.

Distribute the actions *immediately* at the end of the meeting. Ideally use an online tool for recording and sharing actions between groups to obviate the need for this step.

Never assign actions to All. This rarely works, as it doesn't inspire commitment. If necessary, give duplicate actions to the many individuals. This way you can hold individuals to account.

Never give actions to people who are not in the room. Actions are commitments. Absentees can't commit.

The action log requires courage from the chair if it is going to be used effectively. Being bystander-in-chief means that you must intervene regularly in conversations to bring them to conclude with an agreed action. A conversation without an action is only so much air. As a result, my favourite phrase to use in meetings is: "So what's the action coming out of this conversation?" or more succinctly: "What's the next action?". I like this question so much I sometimes distribute it as a handout, or pin it on the wall as a reminder.

Finally, I would urge you once again to move to a shared online platform. The web is full of such services and they are inexpensive. Everyone can have access to the action log 24 hours a day and all changes are seen by everyone immediately. If your choice is good, everyone can use this platform for their own action management. Such a shared to-do list, organised by project will encourage you to save hours of time in your meetings. You can insist, as one of your ground rules, that everyone is familiar with the state of the action log before the meeting starts – and that they have updated their actions – thus obviating the need to review it in any detail during the meeting.

MANAGEMENT REPORT

The DADA model tells us that we need to analyse data in order to make decisions. We should remember W Edwards Deming's quote "In God we trust; all others must bring data". However, the way in which that data is presented is therefore crucial to having an effective meeting.[59] In my experience, there are two common mistakes made with data at meetings. One is to present no data at all, hoping that anecdotes, or recall, will suffice. The other is to present all the data that is available. I have been in meetings where enormous printouts have been used as the main inputs.

Instead, I recommend a format of management report that concentrates the mind of your team and which links directly to the graph that you drew in Exercise 8 in the Committed chapter. The key features of this format are:

A small number of data items, arranged over time – left to right and in descending order of importance. The key performance indicator (there should be only one, at least initially) is at the top.

Two lines for each data item, one above the other – representing Plan and Actual.

The Plan line needs to be filled out with your best estimate – this is a more detailed version of the line from the graph that you created in Exercise 8. The Actual line needs to be filled in as time progresses.

The reason this format works well is that is allows you to *concentrate on what the data is telling you*. To do this, you need to focus primarily on the difference between Plan and Actual.

As the chair of the meeting, these are the questions you should be asking:

- What does the difference mean?
- What is the difference telling us about what is happening?
- What impact will the difference have?
- How do we manage that difference?
- What actions does the difference suggest we should take?

The management report example below has seven lines. Initially, you may only have one. I mentioned earlier the idea of planning for sub-results (individual results which, when taken together, create a larger overall result). If you have planned for several sub-results, then your report will initially contain the overall result and these sub-results and no more. In due course you will no doubt add to and refine the lines on your management report to reflect the complexity of the discussions as you progress.

It is far better to start with a small, very clear, report than to overload the discussions with unnecessary detail. Focusing on results will get you where you want to be.

FIGURE 5: Example management report

Measure	Unit of measure	Resp	Base	Target		Year Jan	Feb	Mar	Apr	May	Jun	Jul	etc	Total
Quality Initiative Programme														
Key Result 1	No	AB	0	100k	Plan	0	0	0	0	0	0	0	0	0
					Actual	0								0
Key Result 2	£	CD	0	124	Plan	0	0	0	0	0	0	0	0	0
					Actual	0								0
Key Result 3	$	EF	0	124	Plan	0	0	0	0	0	0	0	0	0
					Actual	0								0
Subsidiary result 1	no	AB	0	6	Plan	0	0	0	0	0	0	0	0	0
					Actual	0								0
Subsidiary result 2	£	CD	0	124	Plan	0	0	0	0	0	0	0	0	0
					Actual	0								0
Calculated result 1	$	AB	0	30	Plan	0	0	0	0	0	0	0	0	0
					Actual									0
Calculated result 2	no	CD	0	124	Plan	0	0	0	0	0	0	0	0	0
					Actual									0
etc …					Plan									
					Actual									

MEETING EFFECTIVENESS CHECKLIST

As professionals, we are all encouraged to engage in reflective practice. Many of us have reflective entries as part of our professional portfolios. In the same way, I would urge you to spend five minutes at the end of every meeting reflecting on the success or otherwise of the meeting itself. To help this conversation, I use a tool called a Meeting Effectiveness Checklist. This is the tool that will require some courage to introduce as it can seem somewhat alien. My suggestion is that you begin with something very simple, such as that given below. There are more detailed checklists available.

FIGURE 6: Meeting effectiveness checklist

	Max	Actual
Did we use a terms of reference effectively?	10	
Did the meeting run to time and do what was intended?	15	
Did we use an action log effectively?	10	
Did we use data to inform our decisions?	40	
Did we think about our contributions while we were making them?	10	
Did we come to decisions in a balanced fashion?	15	
TOTAL	100	

EXERCISE 13: CHAIR YOUR FIRST DELIVERY TEAM MEETING

Return to your leadership challenge and prepare for your first meeting by doing the following:

- Develop a Terms of Reference and agree it, in full, with the delivery team that you have gathered in Exercise 12.
- Make sure that you discuss and agree a set of ground rules that suits everyone.
- Ensure that everyone has a suitable action-management system and – if you can – find a way to use a shared online system.
- Discuss and agree to the use of a meeting effectiveness score.
- Create a management report with a first-line plan based on the graph that you drew in Exercise 8. Include any sub-results that you may have created when planning in Exercise 10.
- Hold your first meeting and score the meeting, agreeing any actions to improve the next meeting.

When scoring the meeting, gain overall agreement from the attendees and record on the action log anything that arises in the discussion (a projector, a different room, a discussion with an absentee, etc.). If a meeting is repeated regularly, I have found a meeting effectiveness score for each meeting can act as a powerful incentive to improving the meeting as people vie to improve on the previous score. You can even graph the score for more impact.

Top tips for chairing an effective meeting

I hope you will find that chairing a meeting will become much easier when you consider the two models and four tools that I have just presented. The following bullet points are my top tips for running a meeting:

Remember what the meeting is for. You are here to make joint decisions and assign actions.

Keep to time. It's your job to keep your eye on your watch.

Listen instead of talk. Think about the meeting while it's happening and keep your contributions to a minimum. Don't be assertive when you can ask a question instead. Plan your next question rather than contributing.

Concentrate on what the data is telling you. Numbers speak louder than words.

Encourage conversations of possibility and commitment. "What if …" and "I will …". Steer away from conversations of explanation "What happened …".

Ensure everyone has their say. In each conversation, start by asking open questions. Make sure you acknowledge all contributions. Then seek consensus through closed questions. Finally, write down what is agreed as an action.

Balance contributions: Find movers who will come up with ideas (remember that's not your job); seek opposers who will challenge and question those ideas (remember that's not your job); ask for followers who will take up actions and agree to things (remember that's not your job); be the bystander-in-chief – spend time thinking about the meeting and how it's going (remember that is your job).

BALANCE USING DIAMOND FACILITATION

Before we finish this chapter, it may be useful to add one further model, specifically to support this last point about balancing contributions and to help you, as the chair, to manage discussions. Consider that good discussions, where everyone has a chance to contribute, and where decisions are made by consensus, require that everyone contributes. This suggests that conversations tend to expand as you seek opinions through open questions and enquiry, before then levelling out through a period of acknowledgement, before closing down and decisions are agreed using more closed questioning. The model is shown below with some ideas on how to create this type of discussion.

It's difficult to describe how it feels to be part of a well-chaired discussion, but when you witness it, there is no doubt that it feels quite like this – almost like breathing in, pausing, and then breathing out.

Learning to facilitate such discussions takes a little practise. Hopefully this model will help you.

FIGURE 7: Diamond model of facilitation

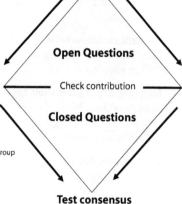

Some Top Tips on:

Questioning
- Use open questions to prompt discussion
- Use probing questions to explore issues
- Use closed questions to seek consensus
- Avoid leading or multiple questions

Listening
- Acknowledge what gets said
- Use verbal and non verbal encouragement
- Bring private conversations into the room
- Bring quiet voices into the room

Clarifying
- Remove confusion by re-phrasing
- Check understanding by asking others to summarise

Focusing
- Maintain focus by pointing out tangents
- Maintain energy by moving the conversation on

Managing behaviour
- Encourage people to speak for themselves, not the group
- Prevent side conversations and hijacking

Reaching consensus
- Manage conflict
- Test assumptions
- Use time as your ally

Introduce subject

Open Questions

Check contribution

Closed Questions

Test consensus

THE LANGUAGE OF ACTION

As a final point in this chapter on action, let me turn once again to the subject of leadership and language. One of my favourite cartoon strips is from Dilbert, the archetypal oppressed office worker. Dilbert is standing at the water cooler with one his co-workers.[60] "I absolutely need your input by Tuesday," he says. "But considering that you're massively unreliable, I'd like to save time by yelling at you now." He pauses and then shouts: "YOU SAID YOU'D DO IT BY TUESDAY!" His co-worker looks up and replies casually, "Um … I was busy." Being too busy is an excuse that we easily recognise as being inadequate – it's like blaming The Management – yet it is nonetheless tempting to use it, often dressed in different clothing: "I've got a lot on my plate at the moment" (everyone else, by contrast, has empty plates); "I just didn't have the time" (everyone else has more time than me). The variants are endless.

What such excuses prevent is a more useful discussion about priorities. As I discussed in shifting the line of control, prioritisation is essential. If something doesn't get done it may be because it was simply given a lower priority than something else. Most people have a seemingly infinite number of things to do. If we are to be compassionate with ourselves and kind to our colleagues, we must recognise that things won't get done, however good our intentions. Which is why an action log, and if possible a shared electronic action log on which we can see everybody's actions, is such a useful tool.

So, I'll finish this chapter by making the rather general suggestion that when talking about actions with your colleagues or even considering them on your own, abandon the sticky problem of time and availability and talk more openly about priorities. The relative position on your to-do list, or on a shared action log, is the most important factor in getting something done.

Remember: the most relevant question is not what are *all* the actions, but what is the *next* action.

RESPONSIVE
Learn to learn

Failures are like mosquitoes. They can be swatted one by one, but they still keep coming. The best remedies are to ... drain the swamps in which they breed.

– James Reason [61]

Not long ago, a twelve-year-old girl presented to a children's ward on which I was working, complaining of increased thirst and increased urine output. We quickly diagnosed new-onset diabetes. I spoke at length with her parents discussing this disease, of which they knew very little and which was now going to play a life-long part in their child's health. I spent time explaining as best I could the complications and considerations of this very significant piece of news. I then took her drug chart to the nursing station and prescribed her first dose of insulin. It was the end of a busy shift and I went home soon afterwards satisfied that I had helped this little girl and her family.

Insulin is a natural hormone which regulates our blood sugar. In diabetic patients, their body's source of insulin has failed, so they require it as a drug. While insulin is life-saving in the right quantities, it must be tightly controlled. Given in overdose it can be rapidly fatal. When I arrived at work the next day I discovered that the previous evening I had inadvertently prescribed the girl four times the required dose.

The child weighed 25 kg. I had calculated her total daily dose – which was supposed to be 0.5 units/kg – by mentally multiplying instead of dividing by 2 so she received 50 units instead of 12.5 units. The nursing staff had not noticed this error and she received both morning and evening doses before my mistake was discovered.

With a simple mathematical bungle – which might have cost me a few marks in a school maths exam – I came close to catastrophically changing the life of this family, either by killing the child or causing her irreversible brain damage. Thankfully she developed no symptoms at all, and close monitoring of her blood sugars was all that she needed. The family were very understanding and felt no need to take the matter further. By contrast, I was distraught. Even today, I still think about how close, and how easily, I came to killing her.

I tell this story – of my closest call as a doctor to causing the death of a patient – for two reasons. The first is because it offers an opportunity to discuss the way we approach patient safety. In recent years there has been much change in our attitudes towards error in healthcare. Until relatively recently, everyone, staff and patients alike, assumed that all healthcare professionals were doing the best they could and that if patients suffered this was probably just bad luck. Many problems could be put down to the patient's condition. On occasion, we had to admit, some errors were clearly the fault of an individual, and that this individual was therefore not trying hard enough. In short, the problem was caused by a bad apple, who then became the subject of an inquiry. If the perpetrator was a doctor, it was usually felt that a quiet word in their ear would suffice to encourage them to make fewer mistakes in the future. If they were from any other profession, however, the reaction could be substantially less tolerant.[62] The remedies would then focus on re-education of the individual involved or, in some cases, the wider workforce. A new policy would be written and emailed to everyone; a poster campaign might be designed. In a triumph of hope over experience, we expected some exhortation and re-education to prevent it happening again.

This is the *person-centred view* of medical error. Thankfully this is changing. Today we are instead beginning to accept that many errors, like my insulin miscalculation, are a natural consequence of being human and that they are to be expected and tolerated. Our response should not be to root out and punish individuals who have made mistakes but instead to mount a vigorous enquiry into the conditions and context that surrounds the error so that we can prevent the circumstances from recurring.

The second reason that I tell the story is because, as we shall see, it serves as a good example of how cause and effect are complex and interconnected. The interdependence of different decisions within the complex institutions in which we work needs to be examined and understood if we are to effect change successfully. All of the complex parts are interconnected in a vast system of decisions, causes, conditions and effects, none of which should be viewed in isolation.

This chapter is therefore largely about how you can do that – how to examine the system and learn when things go wrong. Whether you are dealing with a care delivery problem (CDP), such as my misprescription, or a service delivery problem (SDP), such as when a patient misses their appointment, you will benefit from taking this wider, *systemic view of error* and adapting your response accordingly. This systemic approach is what I mean by being responsive.

The first part of this chapter therefore describes some key patient safety concepts, covering types of error and psychological bias. These concepts are then applied to help you investigate errors or process failures relevant to your leadership challenge. The final section of the chapter describes the concept of Appreciative Inquiry, which I hope will be useful when investigating how your leadership challenge may be improved.

EXERCISE 14: WHAT'S A FAILURE?

Return to your leadership challenge and identify what constitutes an error or failure. What measurable event will undermine success?

For instance, is an error or failure related to an absence of a critical move identified in Exercise 7? Have you identified them in the graphs that you drew in Exercise 8 or the management report you drew up in Exercise 13?

Be clear about when an error or process failure undermines your leadership challenge and agree this with your delivery team.

FIND THE HOLES

The quote which starts this chapter is from James Reason, emeritus professor of psychology at the University of Manchester who has written extensively on the subject of human error across many different industries. It is taken from his short but highly influential paper from 2000 in the

British Medical Journal, in which he exhorts his healthcare readership to see safety incidents as the result of concurrent system failures, rather than simply as errors committed by individuals. He asks us, in other words, to abandon the person-centred view of error.

ERRORS AND VIOLATIONS

Reason's work provides a three-part classification of error, whereby individuals either fail to execute a plan correctly, or execute the wrong plan.

Slips

This is a failure to execute a plan by doing some part of the plan incorrectly. Leaving for work with your house-mate's ID card, rather than your own, would be a slip. My insulin error was a slip. Slips are primarily failures of intent. Solutions to slips, in very general terms, require a change to the design of the environment or system so that slips become either impossible or less likely. Removing a step which involves a calculation, by providing a look-up table, would make a calculation error less likely.

Lapses

This is another failure to execute a plan, but this time by missing out a step. This is usually a failure of memory. Leaving for work without any ID badge at all would be a lapse. Failing to sign a prescription would be a lapse. The solution to lapses – again very generally – is to provide a mechanism whereby a missing step is made more obvious or the following step rendered impossible. Checklists, which we discuss in the Uniform chapter are common mechanisms to ensure that steps are not omitted.

Mistakes

A mistake, by contrast, is a failure to create the correct plan in the first place. Mistakes are usually due to inadequate information or knowledge. Mistakes may also be rule-based – either because a rule is itself wrong, or it is applied inappropriately. Leaving for work on your day-off is a mistake. Making an incorrect diagnosis is a mistake. In general, preventing mistakes requires that we have enough information, knowledge, skills and rules to govern all possibilities.

These three together form what Reason calls active errors. He also identifies another type of unsafe act which is not itself related to a plan and is therefore not deemed an error, as such, namely:

Violations

When we, as caregivers or leaders intentionally go against established protocol, this is considered a violation. If we fail to wash our hands at any point when local policies prescribe it, or if we use a drug that is not indicated by policy, these are violations. This may sound as if all violations are culpable, but some may be expedient. Using an antibiotic against policy because of lack of availability may be a violation, but is likely to be seen as reasonable.[63]

By definition, active errors and violations are to be found close to the sharp end of care delivery where the caregiver and the patient meet. It is easy to see how decisions made at the sharp end can lead to patient harm.

VINCENT'S FIVE FACTORS

However, the real world is much more complex. Building on James Reason's work, Professor Charles Vincent of University College London, another expert on safety and error has provided an analysis of the context for error. He has provided a way of thinking about the overall system in which they occur.[64] He identifies five types of contributory factors which influence the likelihood of error.

These factors are: the working environment, team factors, individual factors, task factors and patient factors.

As a worked example, what follows is an account of the contributory factors that led to the insulin overdose error I described earlier.

Working Environment

What is it like to work in the place where the task is being done. Is it noisy or quiet? How well lit is it? How crowded is it? And how familiar and ergonomic is the layout of the area? What equipment is available?

In my example, I was at the far end of a long ward, away from my other team members. It was well lit, but crowded with paper and computers. A key document about insulin prescription, which would have helped me, was available at the other nursing station, but not where I was sitting. Also, it was shift handover time and there were a group of nursing staff chatting near where I was working.

Team Factors

How well are the team working together? Are there any staffing or personality issues? Does everyone understand their role? Are there any newcomers? Is knowledge readily available within the team?

In my case, I was working without a specialist registrar, because of sickness, so couldn't check with a more experienced colleague. The handover period meant that my prescription ran across two shifts. The oncoming nurses had worked for less time with me, and were unfamiliar with the patient, so may have been less confident in questioning the prescription.

Individual Factors

What is happening to the individual who committed the unsafe act? Are they tired, recently divorced, disabled in some way? Are they fit to do the job? How well trained were they for the task in hand? How many times had they performed it before? Are they physically suited to the task?

This was the first time I had prescribed sub-cutaneous insulin for a child. I was nearing the end of a 13 hour shift. Perhaps my seniority in my home speciality of A&E made me appear more confident than I was. My induction into the department had been inadequate because I didn't know about the insulin folder at the other end of the ward.

Task Factors

What about the task might make it more conducive to error? Are there difficult equipment or complex process steps involved? How complex, time-consuming or impractical is the task? Does it require a lot of cognitive ability? Or is it repetitive and tedious?

I was being asked to do a calculation which involved several arithmetic steps, including dividing the total daily dose into $2/3$ and $1/3$ doses. I was using a policy which was out-of-date because, we discovered, doctors and nurses were using two different computer systems to store policies.

Patient Factors

What aspects of the patient might make error more likely? If they are vulnerable, or shy, or fat, or foreign, or unconscious? Any characteristic can, depending on the task involved, lead to an increase in the likelihood of error.

My patient was a child and had not been previously dosed with insulin. If, by contrast, this had been an experienced, adult diabetic, such an error would very likely have been picked up by the patient themselves.

All these contributory factors, Vincent argues, can be considered as *latent conditions* rather than active errors. They are the breeding grounds where errors, like mosquitoes, multiply. We know, for instance, that every shift change creates a working environment where errors are more likely. In the vast majority of cases, errors are avoided or trapped, but the latent condition of shift change means that if an error is going to happen it is more likely to happen then.

What is less immediately obvious, is that these latent conditions are created by decisions that may be taken far away from the patient, both in distance and time. These decisions are the blunt end of care delivery. The length of a shift, the recruitment and training of new staff, the wording of policies, and the purchasing decisions ... all these are contributory factors in creating latent conditions.

Vincent also describes how the cultural norms of an organisation can have a profound effect on the environment. How we challenge, or fail to challenge, our colleagues; how much help and support we give; how we address each other or refer to patients. All these will also have an effect on the prevalence of error.

To illustrate the effect of these wider contextual factors, I will mention two well-publicised errors from some years ago. In the first, a patient was given a chemotherapy drug into the spinal cord which was intended for intravenous administration [65] and the patient died as a result. Today, such a mix up can be prevented by having equipment with different connectors for different routes. Yet the availability of such connectors is patchy, due to a combination of policy, purchasing and stock-control decisions. The latent errors still exist in some hospitals but not in others.

The other infamous case involved a surgeon who removed the sole healthy kidney from a patient, leaving a diseased organ in place. A medical student realised that the team were operating on the wrong side, but was put down by the operating surgeon who simply said "You're wrong!". A culture which dismisses such an important concern is clearly more dangerous than one where junior staff are taken more seriously, but the factors which cause such a culture to be maintained are difficult to identify. And they certainly do not rest entirely with the individuals involved.

The point is that cultural and organisational factors, despite being very far from the point of care, can have a huge impact on patient safety. The summary of these ideas is shown in the diagram below.

FIGURE 8: The Systemic View of Failure

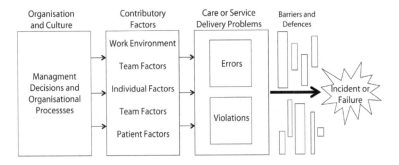

UNDERSTAND YOUR BIASES

It is heartening that many organisations are now making headway against the person-centred view of error in favour of a fairer and more systemic view where error is seen as a part of human nature and where our efforts must therefore be directed to eliminating the latent conditions. To use Reason's metaphor, in many workplaces we are beginning to drain the swamp, rather than swat the mosquitoes.

Sadly, the person-centred view, where individuals are blamed for the consequences of their actions, does still persist. So it is worth spending a few moments thinking about why this is so prevalent, even in the face of clear evidence that it is counter-productive. Psychologists tell us that we are prone to four biases which make the person-centred view our preferred stance.

Hindsight Bias

This prompts us to presume, when looking back at a situation, that we would have acted differently. We believe that *we* would have spotted the warning signs, *we* would have foreseen the outcome that actually transpired. We think "Good lord! How could anyone have been so short-sighted/irresponsible/unhinged as to have made that decision?" Hindsight bias is common. Every day I hear doctors openly criticising each others" decisions or judgments. We use the knowledge of the present to judge the decisions of those who are blinded to the outcome. If you have ever pored over some patient notes, or a report, and shaken your head, asking, incredulously "Why, oh why, did they do that?". The answer is quite simple. Because given the situation and the available information, they genuinely thought it was the right thing to do. Perhaps they were tired, it was dark, the patient was screaming. You should instead assume that in the same circumstances, you could have done the same.

The problem with Hindsight Bias is that our incredulity blinds us to learning. When we see things with the 20/20 vision of hindsight, our questions can easily become unreasonable. Just the other day, I witnessed a conversation between an anaesthetic consultant, recently arrived for a shift, and a very junior ward-based doctor who wanted a deteriorating patient considered for admission to the Intensive Care Unit. The grilling that the young doctor received seemed to take no account of the difficult circumstances in which he was working (poorly supervised with several sick patients) or the fact that he had done his best to raise his concerns earlier in the day. The staccato "why on earth …?" questioning style from the consultant did little to improve anything and only served to reinforce the impression that she thought everyone was an idiot.

So next time you're tempted to raise your eyes to heaven and ask "What were they thinking?" – stop. Ask the question with openness. "Hmmm. I wonder what may have caused that to happen?" With the right attitude of open enquiry, you will discover a more useful answer.

Illusion of Free Will

The second reason we tend to resort to blame is that we believe our actions are consciously chosen. The tedious and repetitive nature of many tasks and the emotional nature of healthcare mean this is often untrue. We actively choose very few of our actions. We follow pre-set mental programmes, or are simply distracted much of the time. I didn't *choose* to write the wrong number of insulin units. And I'm sure you didn't choose to leave your umbrella on the train the other day. What's more, much of how we act is the result of our subconscious drives – the work of our elephant or chimp. The illusion of free will provides one of the foundations of the person-centred view, namely "The Perfection Myth": *if people try hard enough, they will make fewer errors.* Our everyday experience tells us the opposite is true.

Fundamental Attribution Bias

This tells us that it is the fault of someone's personality or character that causes error. Have you ever heard someone say: "typical surgeon", or similar? We all tend to think "People like that are more likely to behave like that". In the minds of some, all doctors are arrogant, and all managers are stupid. Everyone carries with them some prejudices of this sort. I work in a speciality that is considered by many to be populated by workshy and slapdash cretins. At least, that's how it comes across. As was clear from the story about Kane Gorny that I recounted in Part I, any such assumptions about types of people can be dangerous.

The Just World Hypothesis

Finally, we all hold – to some degree or other – the assumption that the world is basically fair and that, at some level, bad things only happen to bad people. This gives rise to another pillar of the person-centred view, "The Punishment Myth". This tells us: *if we punish people for making errors, they will make fewer of them.* We may know logically that this is wrong, but it is easy to slip into believing this at an individual level: "If we just removed this accident-prone person, our incidents would improve". Sadly, they are likely to be replaced by someone else, equally as prone to error. The just world hypothesis is not only poisonous, it can also be counter-productive.

You may, of course, think that you personally are free of all such biases. Before you congratulate yourself, let me ask you a question. When I suggested that a most common response to patient safety incidents was to blame individuals, did you think that was a bad thing? Did you think, perhaps, that the people who acted this way were themselves to blame in some way for doing so? Did you thereby unconsciously blame the blamers? Did you think: "I would never blame people" (Hindsight Bias); "They should do things differently?" (Illusion of Free Will); "That's typical of management types!" (Fundamental Attribution Bias) or "If we could just rid ourselves of people that think that way …" (Just World Hypothesis). I'd be surprised if at least one of those sentiments didn't occur to you, at least in passing. Our biases are powerful and ever-present.

As a result, we still see examples of individuals being named and blamed and held to account for errors that any of us could make any day. And when the outcome is serious, the just-world hypothesis exerts itself more strongly. Victims and families want justice. And justice often demands that a perpetrator be punished. The more terrible the outcome, the more pressure is brought to bear to seek out individuals who can be held to account. I know my life would have been very different if the young girl I overdosed had died.

FIND YOUR DATA

Which brings us to the question of how we should respond to failure. As I said earlier, my suggestion is that we should respond similarly whether the failure is primarily a recognisable care delivery problem (CDP) such as a patient falling, or a service delivery problem (SDP) such as a patient missing their appointment. Either way, we should respond systemically – in other words, we should set up or change systems of work rather than pursue the individuals involved. If a patient falls, or fails to show up for an appointment, the temptation (using a person-centred view, coloured by a good dose of fundamental attribution bias) is to assume that the patient is at fault. This assumption blinds us to the contributory factors. Instead, we need to establish where this failure sits as part of a wider context and thereby identify the latent conditions that have brought it about.

In Exercise 14 at the beginning of this chapter, I asked you to identify what constituted a failure or error in the context of your leadership challenge. Now I am asking you to consider how these failures cause the discrepancy between your plan (what we would like to be happening) and actual (what is happening). Whether we are measuring patient falls or missed appointments, our first task is to capture the contextual data about *all* of our failures: when, where and under what circumstances did these failures arise.

I emphasise the word *all*, because if we restrict ourselves to only that small subset of failures where there is a bad outcome (the patient is harmed, or the patient complains) then we will have very little information.

Most errors do not result in harm, so recording harm-only errors means we are only working with a small sub-set of failures. While we should be thankful if only a tiny fraction of patient safety incidents result in harm, this can lead us into complacency, assuming "that always happens, so it is not important". This, in turn, makes us less willing to gather data about no-harm incidents or minor failures. If we do anything, we tend merely to count them (i.e. we had 5 falls and 200 DNAs this month).

As a result, I can almost guarantee you do not currently have enough data to solve your leadership challenge – at least, not in a format or in a place that you can easily use. If you did, it is likely you would be successfully managing the issue and your leadership challenge would not have arisen. So your first task is to capture the right level of data about *all* your failures or errors, not as a one off but as a continuous and reliable stream that you can use day-on-day or week-on-week. You will, in all probability, like Vanessa with her tear-off slip, need to install new system elements or process steps to capture everything you need – and this may require you to find ingenious ways of capturing any data that you don't yet have.

To illustrate this point, let us consider the problem of mis-prescribing medications, more generally. If we only capture medication errors that harm the patient, then we are missing a whole host of data that would help us understand when and how medication errors are made. If you really want to understand where medication errors come from, you need to capture all the near misses, fumbles and quick corrections that take place every day. Anyone who prescribes by hand knows that they can mis-write drugs.[66] Their errors are usually picked up immediately, crossed out and rewritten. Often they are discovered when checked by the dispensing nurse or pharmacist. These fumbles are not even near misses. They are, if anything, distant misses. And they are almost never captured, so we have no idea how prevalent our active errors really are. As a result, we have no hope of understanding the latent conditions which cause them. To really understand medication errors, we need to ask prescribers and dispensers to record *every* time they make even the slightest error. Difficult? Not technically. But if this were your leadership challenge, you're likely going to have a huge hill to climb installing a new culture of prescriber error reporting. You would need all your Commitment, Energy and Focus (all three of these chapters will help) just to get the data you need to understand the few errors that actually cause harm.

Many leadership challenges revolve around the issue of data. Often you will need to start with what you have – which may be inadequate and incomplete – and then work outwards. To return to our outpatient example, if DNA appointments merely have a date and time, that may be a good start. However, very soon, you might decide that you need to add the patient's age, distance from the clinic, and number of co-morbidities. Suddenly you realise, you need to know how mobile they are physically, and what level of transport they have available and … "Oh dear, we don't record that".

EXERCISE 15: CAUSATIVE NUMBERS

Return to your leadership challenge and the top-line measure of success that you devised in the Committed chapter, and which you put into your management report (as described in the Active chapter). Add another line to show the errors or failures that you identified in Exercise 14.

Now ask what you think may be the factors that could create the successes and failures that contribute to that top-line figure. Choose a handful of the easiest or most obviously relevant.

Enter these items as data-lines on your management report and estimate the plan figures for these lines, consistent with your top-line number.

Identify how you might measure these.

You will find that you will start to gather new data as you become more aware of the factors that influence where your errors and failures are occurring.

ABANDON YOUR SEARCH FOR THE ROOT CAUSE

Once you have captured enough data, you will be able to start a discussion about what the data is telling you. My suggestion is to do this in decision-making meetings whose purpose is to deliver the result. You will be looking at how the failures influence the difference between your plan (what you want to happen) and the actual (what happens in reality). I have discussed these sorts of meetings in detail in the Active chapter.

However, you may soon find that this is not enough. The outcome of a single failure may be so serious as to warrant a separate Serious Incident (SI) investigation.[68] Or, you may have too much data, with too much complexity, or you may need to widen and deepen your understanding beyond what could be done in a single meeting. If so, then you could benefit from undertaking a Root Cause Analysis (RCA).

Unfortunately, the RCA process is often derided in healthcare organisations, and not without reason. A propensity for the person-centred view of error can make a mockery of a process that is intended to uncover the systemic reasons for failure. As a junior doctor once quipped to me: "RCA? Isn't that just another word for witch-hunt?" Even when the investigators consider, in good faith, that they are seeking the root causes, they are often constrained by their own biases, or lack of time, authority and understanding. The result is usually that they concentrate on factors which are close to the incident. The effect is the same. Individual errors are highlighted, rather than the systems which gave rise to those errors. What I am proposing here is the antidote to this.

Before I set out my preferred approach, we need first to establish two uncomfortable truths, both of which are highly relevant to all RCA investigations. The first is this: *there is no single root cause*. For any one error or care delivery problem (CDP) there will be multiple causative factors (CFs), as I have tried to illustrate with my own example. If you wish, you can call them root causes (plural), but causative factor is more accurate. Sidney Dekker has written extensively about the psychology of error, drawing on long years as an innovative thinker and writer. He was for many years an airline pilot, and is now a professor at Griffith University in Australia and founder of the Safety Science Innovation Lab. In his book, *The Field Guide to Understanding "Human Error"*, he puts it this way:

> *We think there is something like the cause of a mishap (sometimes we call it the root cause, or the primary cause), and if we look in the rubble hard enough, we will find it there. The reality is that there is no such thing as the cause, or primary cause or root cause. Cause is something we construct, not find.* [69]

The second uncomfortable fact, implied by the title of Professor Dekker's book, is this: *there is no such thing as human error*. Or rather, there is no point considering human error as a useful description of a causative factor. We all make a great many mistakes, for all sorts of reasons. It is finding the reasons that is important. Simply putting a mistake down to human error is lazy thinking. And it is a person-centred, rather than systemic view.

If we accept these two uncomfortable facts, then the process of RCA takes on a very different favour. Instead of looking inward and downward for more and more detail about the incident itself – useful though that may be initially – we are instead trying to look outward and upward and further backward to gather the most comprehensive view of the context in order to construct the nexus of causes. This may seem more complex but it is not. It is merely a different emphasis. I can assure you that the most significant difficulty you are likely to face will be the expectations and attitudes of people who are looking for a single root cause and, by extension, a culprit.

How, then, do we organise such a system-orientated investigation? The best method that I have come across is from Inpractice Training, a group of lawyers who teach healthcare professionals how to do such investigations and who undertake such investigations themselves. Their approach is to create a series of diagrams they call Wagon Wheels.[67]

DRAW YOUR WAGON WHEELS

The principle behind wagon wheels is simple. We are looking for a systemic response to any failure, so we should be investigating the system. Which means that the output from our investigation must give an answer to the question "What systems were inadequate or missing in order to allow the failure to happen?". The wagon wheel is the route to that answer.[70]

At the centre of the wagon wheel we place the failure that occurred. This should be the care delivery or service delivery problem (CDP or SDP) that you have identified. For any one incident, there may be more than one of these, so you will have several wagon wheels for any one investigation.

Let me return to my own insulin overdose error to provide an example. The words Insulin Overdose go into a circle, representing the hub. We now need to add the spokes. These are arrows, each of which connects a single causative factor (CF) to the hub. In my example, I have already mentioned several of these in the discussion above. Among them are: two sets of standards for nurses and doctors; a diabetes folder at only one nursing station; need for a mental calculation; a doctor who had not undergone local induction.

Finally, and most importantly, we now need to annotate the spokes, by indicating across each one, the missing or inadequate systems that allowed that CF to contribute to the failure. The words that annotate the spokes will drive your recommendations – what you, as the investigator, believe to be the necessary systemic changes that will prevent the error from recurring.

In my example, I can suggest several such changes. These might include: a suitable, unitary electronic storage system for protocols and policies; a system for monitoring where physical/printed policy documents and folders are kept and updated; a policy document which provides a lookup table, obviating the need for mental calculation; a system for monitoring local induction completion.

Figure 9: Example Wagon Wheel diagram

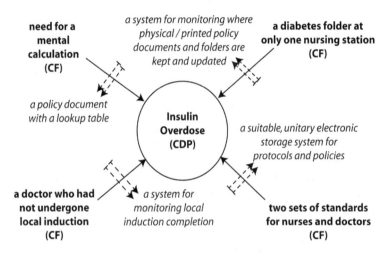

You may think that putting in place all those changes in response to an error that caused no harm would be something of an over-reaction. A moment's reflection, however, should convince you that if the latent conditions still exit, then the opportunity for error still exists. Next time, the young child, their family and another trainee doctor, may not be so lucky.

Putting these sorts of systemic changes in place are what Liam Donaldson, the former Chief Medical Officer of England has called "a strong response to a weak signal of failure".[71] I am sad to report that my employer implemented none of these changes, and I soon afterwards discovered two doctors, calculators in hand, poring over the same document that had contributed to my own error. My employer's weak response (they did nothing) laid the ground for further errors and perhaps the death of a child on their ward.

EXERCISE 16: WAGON WHEEL PROCESS

Identify an event which constitutes a failure within the context of your leadership challenge. This need not be a serious incident, but should represent a failure which is representative, and complex, enough to offer up some good lessons.

Start by drawing out a tabular time-line of events that led up to the failure. Go back as far as possible in time (this might include a few years, to when a policy was issued, or an employee was inducted). For each such event provide as much information as possible. If the event itself is a Care Delivery Problem (CDP) or Service Delivery Problem (SDP), mark it as such. For each of these identify as many Contributory Factors (CFs) as you can.

When all the data is collated, call a meeting with your delivery team and together draw out a wagon wheel diagram for each CDP/SDP, identifying the missing or inadequate system elements thrown up by your investigation. Now list your recommendations based on these.

Please note that the data-collection phase of this exercise will take you longer – much longer – than the drawing out of the wagon wheel diagram or deciding on systemic changes. That is to be expected. The more thorough and well tabulated your data, the easier your wagon wheels will be to draw.

APPRECIATIVE ENQUIRY: THE LANGUAGE OF POSITIVITY

In the last two sections, and in the Active chapter, I have encouraged you to gather people together to make decisions and to investigate some root causes. The question that arises is how can we best use these meetings, given how much we rely on them, to generate positivity, particular given some of our natural biases towards negativity. When we focus on problems and investigations, as we have done in this chapter, we run the risk of creating an atmosphere of anxiety. Can we instead generate a positive conversation that promotes the creativity and enthusiasm that is necessary to improve our latent conditions and trap our active errors?

I strongly believe we can, and to understand how, we should turn the clock back to 1979, where a 24-year-old doctoral student, David Cooperrider, was working at the Cleveland Clinic in Ohio.

The Cleveland Clinic is one of the top four medical institutions in the United States. It is one of the most highly recognised centres for medical research and practice. Cooperrider's doctoral thesis was, however, not focused on anything directly related to medical science. He was a behavioural social science student from Case Western Reserve University, based just a few blocks away, engaged in organisational research (OR was a buzzword back then). He was engaged in a programme to find out what was wrong with the culture at the clinic. Within a few short weeks, however, he had discovered something extraordinary. There was, in fact, nothing wrong with the culture. On the contrary, the clinic provided an example of the opposite: an extraordinary view of "positive cooperation, innovation and egalitarian governance". This excited the young researcher so much that he changed the focus of his PhD in order to describe what made this possible. The result of this PhD, and the series of articles and books that followed, burgeoned not just into a stellar academic career for Cooperrider and his mentor Suresh Srivastva,[72] but also spawned an organisational development approach called Appreciative Inquiry or AI.[73]

AI has proponents and expert teachers who are better placed than me to give a more detailed account of the subject. What I can offer is an outline of the key ideas in the hope that you can start to use them yourself. Cooperrider describes his research at the Cleveland Clinic as showing "a Heisenberg observer effect on steroids – how just the mere act of inquiry can change the world". He demonstrated very clearly that the way that the staff at the Cleveland Clinic asked questions about the future has a radical effect on the outcome they achieved. He found that if we ask "What's the problem?" we will think mainly about problems and their sequels. As a result, our future will be mired in the language of problems and our responses to them. If, on the other hand, we ask "What did we do well?" – which is what the staff at the Cleveland were routinely doing – we can *generate* an altogether more positive future, steeped in the recognition of success.

It is this principle which underpins the use of positive language that I have been urging in leadership rounds, thank-you letters and talking up: such language creates a different result. By asking positive questions and saying positive things, you can *create* a better future for you, your colleagues and your patients. All this may sound like happy-clappy pop psychology. But it's worth reflecting upon what the effect of repeated and sustained doses of positivity might have in creating an overall shift in organisational culture in favour of positivity and better results. There are now four decades of respectable research that shows this does happen.[74]

From your own experience, it may be worth thinking once again about your favourite leader from the exercise at the beginning of this book. How did they approach things? How did they ask questions? What was their mood? And how did they present you to others? Did they big you up? Make you feel good? If you wanted to work hard for them, was this part of the reason?

AI tells us that if we focus on the positive, and are positive with those around us, things will improve.

How can you use AI with your leadership challenge? AI is not a technique or a methodology, partly because Cooperrider himself was keen to avoid pigeonholing his discovery. However, there are some principles which I have found useful, which stem from Cooperrider's early work:

Be appreciative

Ensure the questions you ask seek out the positive. Cooperrider and his colleagues mention trying to establish "What gives life?" to a situation. What is it that gives people a good feeling, makes them want to come to work, makes them want to work with *you*? This is reflected in the work by the Heath brothers, mentioned in the Introduction. Find the feeling. Focus on what makes people feel good by seeking out the best.

I think in healthcare it is sometimes difficult to make this shift towards appreciation, given our habit of diagnosing disease and identifying patient safety failures and our tendency to seek out and eliminate what is bad. We must try harder not to focus on the single negative feature in a vast plain of excellence. If you want a quick example, of what I mean, try this: write the following series of sums on a piece of paper:

$$1 \times 1 = 1$$
$$2 \times 2 = 4$$
$$3 \times 3 = 9$$
$$4 \times 4 = 15$$
$$5 \times 5 = 25$$

Now show it to a colleague and ask what they see. Most will quickly point out that 4×4 is 16, not 15. Now ask them why they have ignored four correct answers. Some people can become irritated by this question. For them, the error is the only feature.

The trick – as with most aspects of leadership – is to practise a new language. In order to counter our inherent bias towards problems and negativity, we need to make the language of appreciation a habit in all our communications and in all our meetings. Whether we are writing emails, chairing a meeting, running a workshop or simply walking the floors, we need to concentrate on what is good, what is working, what is great about a new idea, what is excellent about an individual, what is exciting about a new possibility.

To do so authentically you'll need to learn and practise this language of appreciation. You'll need to practise saying "That's great", "Well done", "I love that", "You're amazing", "We did so well today", "How do we capture the great stuff that you're doing?" and so on. Even the smallest remark can be turned to your advantage by creating positivity. For instance, the difference may seem small, but in response to a new idea presented in a meeting, saying "OK. Anyone else got any ideas?" which is neutral and potentially dismissive could so easily be: "That's a great idea. Let's work on that."

Be applicable

Ensure that you tackle what is relevant and important to people. Frame your leadership challenge in the language and context that is relevant to them. We all have a tendency to assume that what is important to us will be important to others. The most common mistake and one which is perpetrated too often, is to use financial arguments with clinicians. If you can link financial implications to patient outcomes or patient experience, you stand a better chance of generating positive responses.

Be provocative

Find ways to be compelling. Come up with ideas that challenge and excite the people you are engaging. This seems self-evident, yet it is so often missed. As I will suggest in the Leading chapter, people are excited by the prospect of being first or best and being part of a team or organisation that strives to do the best. In your meetings, if you encourage provocative ideas, you will create a degree of positivity that will help gain momentum.

Be collaborative:

Ensure that you are inclusive and egalitarian. Ask yourself who is going to be affected by your leadership challenge. How can you elicit their help in generating solutions? How are you going to get feedback from them? Using Appreciative Inquiry, you can begin to break down the barriers within and around your organisation or your department. The constituency affected by your leadership challenge, and their influence, may be much wider than you expect.

Before we finish this discussion of AI, I should counter the objection that this chapter has hitherto been focused almost exclusively on error and process failure. AI doesn't suggest that we ignore latent conditions and opportunities for error. We need to know what has gone wrong. But how we fix it is another matter. The principals of AI suggest that in order to reduce our errors we need to focus our discussions predominantly on what works well, and to measure our successes as avidly as our failures. The most common example of this, I have found, is the almost fetish-like focus we have for patient complaints. Complaints tell us important facts, but our obsession is rarely balanced by a similar focus on patient compliments. We seem to have no hesitation in berating our staff on the rare occasions that things go badly yet almost never thank or congratulate them when things go well.

ENERGETIC
Develop your team

When people are in fear, they don't want to go to work ... When you work, you want a happy crew going down the road together.

– DAVID LYNCH[75]

Stephen McKernan is a teacher who I met a few years ago. He grew up in Northern Ireland during the "The Troubles" of the 1970s, a time when the social separation between the Catholic and Protestant communities was near absolute. It is hard for anyone outside the area to comprehend the almost total segregation which existed at that time. The entire country was divided by violence, street by street, and village by village.

McKernan and his family survived the troubles unscathed. He did well at school and then, after university, trained as a primary school teacher. His first jobs were in schools that, by default, taught children from just one side of this divide. He very soon realised how much the mindset that had created the troubles was being perpetuated right here, in his classroom.

Although much hope for change was pinned on the Good Friday Agreement of 1998, the thawing of political tensions provoked very little change in communities or schools. So, in 2003, McKernan decided that enough was enough. He found his integrity was being stretched with each day he taught in this polarising environment. So he resigned in order to join the Integrated Education Movement, a group of schools whose aim is to educate children from both Protestant and Catholic traditions together, as well as those from other faiths and none. He was prepared to ignore the sectarian divide, to challenge the ignorance at the heart of the troubles. Such a move required bravery and commitment in the face of the ingrained hatred and the threat of violence that had kept communities apart for so many years.

At the time, there were fewer than 30 integrated schools in the entire province – educating less than three per cent of primary school children. McKernan decided to build a new one. From scratch. He gained permission to erect a single portable cabin in a car park in Cookstown, a large village in the centre of Northern Ireland with a significant mixture of Protestants and Catholics. He then set about recruiting parents from among the several hundred families in the area who had children aged five or six. He wrote to every family and visited anyone willing to listen. Every parent realised that segregated education would have a negative effect on the peace process, and therefore, in the long run, on their child. But they were universally worried: how would sending their child to a new integrated school appear to their neighbours? Did this risk ostracising them and their children from other families? Did it risk violence being perpetrated against their family? Could they take that risk, given all that had happened in the past?

PHOENIX PRIMARY SCHOOL

In the end, the Phoenix Primary School, Cookstown, opened in September 2004 with just seven children. McKernan was their only teacher. The next year there were 17 new entrants. After that, there was no stopping it. The school intake continued to grow every year and within just six years, until McKernan handed over the headship, the school was teaching over 220 children in all seven primary school years, and had a waiting list for places. In 2009 the school was rated by the Office for Standards in Education (OFSTED) as outstanding – the highest accolade that the regulator can bestow.

I visited the Phoenix Primary School towards the end of McKernan's tenure there. What struck me most forcibly was the extraordinary enthusiasm and dedication that he generated in his teachers and pupils alike. He was, in my view, the epitome of a CAREFUL leader. Not only were his commitment, capacity for action and ability to learn and adapt all clearly there, but also his *energy* was infectious. This energy seemed to create opportunities around him and inspire effort from those around him. It's not just that his staff and pupils were following him – although clearly he was the leader of this very special school – it was more that they were being nurtured and encouraged so that they felt more successful and happy. There was a mixture of robust enthusiasm, confidence and industriousness that was almost tangible. This was not high energy. The kids were not shouting or doing high-fives. No one was pumped. There was no fear. Everyone was heard. Everyone was present.

As I wandered around, it occurred to me forcibly that this environment was therapeutic.[76] Could we, I wondered, find a way to replicate this energy within our own healthcare institutions? If so, I thought, many of the challenges we face would be more easily addressed. How, I wondered, could we bring a little bit of McKernan's energy to our own world and, specifically, to our own leadership challenges?

This chapter is an attempt to answer that question.

AUTHENTICITY

Our first subject is a short discussion of *authenticity,* which McKernan describes as the most important concept we can teach a child. We then move on to discuss something about teams and their formation, which we then use as the basis for discussing four important leadership skills which can engender the sort of energetic environment in which we would all like to work. We will then finish with a short discussion and exercise concerning the relationship between attitude and results.

GET RELATED, BE AUTHENTIC

When talking about his work – and particularly his relationship with his students – the word McKernan most commonly uses is *authenticity.* He sees this as the bedrock of all his relationships. He uses this word even with his youngest students, aged five or six, and they understand quite clearly what he means. I reflect – as I did when I mentioned "talking up" – that our inner chimp is fine-tuned by millions of years of evolution to any signs of danger. In my view, this is why we pick up very quickly on any *inauthenticity* in others, even when we are very young.

Research supports McKernan's view that authenticity is important in leaders. In an extensive and powerful piece of research based on feedback from over 2,000 National Health Service leaders[77] Beverley Alimo-Metcalfe, Professor of Leadership Studies at the University of

Leeds, identified authenticity as one of the six personal factors that create successful leaders.[78]

McKernan talks repeatedly about having authentic conversations, where nothing is missing, under the surface, or kept back. He says that his task as a leader, above all else, is to ensure that all his staff and pupils have authentic conversations, all the time. When watching him at work I see him declare a great deal of "unsaid stuff". This may be as simple as acknowledging someone as they enter or leave a room, not allowing them to be both present and absent. Or it may be more complicated, exploring perhaps some resentment visible in a facial expression or body language. He also verbalises very clearly what he feels and what he has noticed. The result is that everyone in his company is clear. There is no side. No games.

McKernan says his aim is to ensure that his team members develop, maintain and manage all their relationships with authenticity. His view is that the confidence we have in our relatedness to each other is what drives our sense of trust in others. Relatedness is not possible without authenticity. Work is not possible without trust. Authenticity therefore underpins our capacity to work together effectively.[79]

In my view, it is this relentless pursuit of authenticity which is the foundation upon which we must build the energy in our own working environments.

What does this mean for you, in your leadership? I suggest it means using the words *authentic* and *authenticity* more often than perhaps you are used to. It means exploring and examining the nature of your relationships and recognising where you may be lacking relatedness and therefore authenticity. It also means examining, where possible, how you come across to others (if you're wondering how best to find that out, the answer is simply to ask). It means working harder where relatedness and authenticity may be lacking. Relatedness comes from being close to someone personally. This must involve investing time in a relationship with them. It may also involve being honest in situations where honesty is difficult: owning up to feelings and experiences that may not ordinarily expressed. I wouldn't counsel telling everyone what you think of them – that's not necessarily helpful. But sharing your point of view, without making it too personal, can help. Primarily I think being authentic means striving to maintain the same sense of who you are, irrespective of whose company you are in.

EXERCISE 17: RELATIONSHIP MAP

Take a piece of paper and draw four concentric circles. Label these Daily, Weekly, Monthly and Yearly. Divide the circles roughly into three segments, as in a pie. Label these segments: Work, Family, Community.

Now consider each of the people with whom you regularly come in contact. Place their name in the relevant sector, at a distance from the centre which represents approximately how often you interact. Now draw around their name a shape which most closely represents the importance and the nature of your relationship. The more important the relationship, the larger the shape. The more difficult the relationship the more irregular, or spiky, the shape should be.

For instance, you may have a small, smooth shape labeled "Postman" in the Community segment, somewhere near the Weekly contour. You could perhaps have two big spiky shapes in the personal segment, marked "Aunt Selma" and "Aunt Patty".

When you've finished, this is your personal relationship map. You are at the centre of this diagram.

For the purposes of this discussion, we are interested primarily in the shapes you draw in the work segment. Who are the largest, the spikiest and nearest? Return to the discussion on authenticity and relatedness and ask yourself how you might become more related and more authentic with these people.

I will leave you with one final thought on relatedness and authenticity. In most cases, when people change jobs, they leave their boss, not their job. I'm not sure how this resonates with your own experience, but I see this frequently in my work with leaders. And the main reason why people leave their boss is because they don't relate well to them. This is worth a test: when your immediate supervisor, director or leader acts in a way you dislike, how do you manage that? Do you make this clear? If not, then you lack the relatedness to be authentic with them. This allows their behaviour to continue unchallenged. If, as a result, you often think you want to move jobs, my point is made.

Now do another test. Do your direct reports, and the people you lead, have the relatedness to you that allows them to challenge you? If not, they will leave. As a result, you will undoubtedly lose good people. The solution is easier than trying to replace lost talent and knowledge: work on your authenticity.

REACT TO THE STAGES OF TEAM DEVELOPMENT

I'm going to return to the theme of authenticity and your personal style at the end of this chapter, but before then, I am going to introduce some more practical advice around some specific skills, all of which will be necessary for you to create a team with the right energy.

Before I start to describe these, I'd like you to take a moment to think about the questions posed in the next exercise. Your answers will be useful to the ensuing discussion.

EXERCISE 18: FOUR TEAMS

What follows are the descriptions of four teams:

A. A newly formed group that have been asked to work on a project, but who have only just met.

B. A group of individuals who have worked together for a while, who are now having difficulty delivering. They may have differences of opinion on how the team should function. They may also have acquired new members or a new leader.

C. A team that has been working together for long enough to ensure the work is being done to a reasonable standard. There is little change to contend with.

D. A team that is highly adapted to challenges and changes in their work and who are working at maximum capacity, delivering consistently excellent standards of work.

Now try to answer the following questions:

A. What adjectives would you use to describe how it *feels* to be a member of each of these different teams?

B. What behaviours do you think you would observe if you were to study these different teams closely?

C. Can you categorise the teams that you lead, or of which you are a member as fitting one of these four descriptions?

D. If you have assembled a team to address your Leadership Challenge, which of these descriptions fits this team most closely?

In 1965, an educational psychologist called Bruce W Tuckman wrote a paper on team dynamics called "Developmental Sequence in Small Groups". Primarily a literature review, it proposed a model of team development of four stages that were dubbed: "Testing and Dependence", "Intragroup Hostility", "Development of Group Cohesion" and "Functional Role Relatedness". Thankfully – and probably a reason for its subsequent success – the paper gave shorthand words for these stages: *Forming, Storming, Norming and Performing*. Decades of subsequent research have vouched for the fact that, in small groups, many of the psychodynamic processes initially described by Tuckman do take place. In the exercise above, you may have realised, the four descriptions are intended as shorthand for teams in these stages.

Since Tuckman's original paper, this four-stage model has been used extensively within management and leadership programmes to explain how teams evolve. I was first introduced to the model many years ago, during a leadership programme where the stages and their attendant behaviours were provided without much commentary.

FIGURE 10: Stages of team development: What you see and do

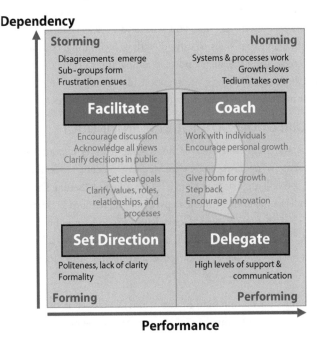

It was only some years later that I was presented with the model together with descriptions of what leaders should strive to do under each circumstance. It is these leadership responses – each a different skill – which, in my view, is the whole point. What follows is my interpretation of that model, and those skills.[80]

In the model, there are four quadrants representing the four stages. Progress represented by the large circular arrow in the centre. It is important to realise that team dynamics can flow in both directions, a point made clear in Tuckman's original paper.

The top two quadrants require, as we shall discuss, substantially more leadership time and effort than the bottom two. This is represented by the axis labelled "Dependency". The two left hand quadrants represent the initial stages of team development, which are broadly less effective than the two on the right, hence the other axis labelled "Performance". The overall qualities of the team and the suggested skills of the leader at each stage are given in the relevant quadrants.

The objective of this model is to offer you a way of thinking about the groups in which you work, so that when confronted with a particular set of behaviours, you can identify the stage at which the group is operating and then act appropriately. To do this, you will need to select and deploy one of four critical leadership skills: setting direction, facilitating, coaching and delegating. Recognising the stage and responding appropriately is critically important. Choosing the wrong intervention (delegating instead of setting direction, for instance) will cause your team's performance to deteriorate.

SETTING DIRECTION: DON'T JUST POINT, INDUCT

"Forming" is the stage when teams are young. This is characterised by politeness, a sense of openness to new ideas, and a dependence on the leader. At this stage, the skill most needed from a leader is that of "Setting Direction". There is a model from another American psychologist, Richard Beckhard, who proposed in 1972 that teams need "Goals, Roles, Processes and Interpersonal Relationships". Using this classification, it is worth checking that all members of your team have a clear understanding and agreement of this model.

Goals

What is the mission or outcome of the team? We covered this in some detail in the chapter on Commitment. I won't labour the point.

Roles

Who does what? Who has responsibility for what part of the team's responsibilities?

Processes

How does "stuff get done"? How are the important elements of the group's responsibilities carried out? How do these relate to the wider world?

Interpersonal relationships

How do we manage relationships within the group? What happens if there are disagreements? How do team members communicate with each other? How do they communicate issues with you, the leader?

Setting direction is not as simple as simply pointing to the top of the mountain. We also need to choose our route, we need to establish who is going to manage the stores and so on. If you want an easy way to remember this, simply ask yourself what you would from a corporate induction programme. The basic questions are: Why are we here? What is my job? How do I claim my expenses (or other admin necessities)? Who to go to if I need help?

EXERCISE 19: DEFINE YOUR DIRECTION

Define the Goals, Roles, Processes and Interpersonal Relationships for the action team you are going to use for your Leadership Challenge (or for any other relevant group). Check with others in the group that they agree.

FACILITATION: GRASP THE NETTLE OF DISAGREEMENT

*"Je mets en fait que, si tous les hommes savaient ce qu'ils disent
les uns des autres, il n'y aurait pas quatre amis dans le monde."
(I contend that if everyone were to know who said what to
whom, there would be no four friends in the world.)*
– BLAISE PASCAL, PENSÉES (SECTION II, 101)

I once worked in a hospital where the interpersonal relationship between two senior surgeons had been allowed to deteriorate to such an extent that they were unable to be in the same room as each other.

The entire surgical department and its operations were scheduled and organised in such a way that no patient or member of staff was allowed to cross the invisible barrier that had grown between them. Woe betide the junior doctor who inadvertently gave advice or treatment to a patient on the other side. Such behaviour seems incredible, but it was not so many years ago. It is the most extreme example I have ever come across of a group that had been left to fester in the storming stage of team development.

Tuckman's model tells us that the initially polite and reserved period of Forming inevitably gives way to a period when team members start to clash. Differences of opinion, personal style or emphasis will emerge and friction will inevitably arise. These disagreements, if left untended, will mature into cliques and from there into full-blown schisms. The level of relatedness within the team will disappear entirely under the weight of disagreement. It is sufficiently common that few will have escaped the consequences of storming. It is an uncomfortable phase, which, if not managed effectively, can perpetuate and even increase levels of hostility between members and sub-groups.

Storming is not enjoyable. It is challenging for the team and for the leader. Many leaders will shy away from it. This can be a disaster. Storming must be addressed, not ignored.

The leadership skill needed at this point is facilitation.

What is facilitation in this context? My view is that it must involve airing and resolving differences between groups and individuals *in front of the whole group*. You may be tempted to try to resolve inter-personal conflicts through one-on-one agreements made in the quiet and safety of your office. This will almost certainly prove counter-productive if not downright poisonous. You will have had a conversation with only one side. You will soon be visited by another individual, representing an alternative view. Within a short time, you will be inundated with similar meetings to resolve every difference that arises. The group won't learn to resolve disagreement internally, and meanwhile, around the water-cooler, any discrepancies you may have introduced will be chewed over. Your authenticity will be under scrutiny and you are unlikely to come out well.

As the model suggests, facilitation is much more complicated and time-consuming for the team leader than setting direction. And it's emotional too. The interpersonal conflict will inevitably affect you, the leader, so it becomes more personally risky. For all these reasons, facilitation is often avoided. If avoided for too long, storming can deteriorate into open hostility.

Thankfully there is a cure, at least in the early stages. And that cure is openness. Usually all that is required for a team that is storming is a meeting in which differences are aired and decisions agreed among the whole group. This requires the skills of chairmanship and diamond facilitation outlined in the Active chapter.

The reason that group discussions will eventually resolve any differences is because agreements made in the open cannot then be rescinded by dissatisfied members of the group. This is a function of Cialdini's "Commitment and Consistency". We can't say one thing in public and then pretend we didn't mean it.

While the diamond model of facilitation may suffice for most situations, there are some situations that require more nuance and preparation. In such cases, I would recommend exploring the Missing Conversations model.[81]

THE MISSING CONVERSATIONS MODEL

You can consider this an expanded – or perhaps upgraded – version of the diamond model. It breaks all our conversations down into one of five types, which are described in more detail below. It is called the Missing Conversations model because it suggests that people behave in different ways depending on which of these conversations they may have missed. It suggests that to feel satisfied with a situation, we need all five conversations and, crucially, they need to be in the right order. If we fail to have all the conversations in the correct order, we tend to exhibit behaviours which reflect the missing conversation. Our job as leaders is to spot conversations which are missing for an individual or group and then use suitable enquiry, acknowledgement and advocacy in order to supply the missing conversation. The model below provides some prompts for suitable questions or statements.

FIGURE 11: The missing Conversations Model

Relatedness
"What do we think?"
Building relationships between people; ensuring
that everyone's views are taken into account

Exploration
"What could we do?"
Exploring possibilities together; being creative;
discovering new things

Decisions
"What shall we do?"
Making decisions on direction; agreeing on
way forward; formulating opportunities

Actions
"Who will do what when?"
Sharing out the workload; clarifying roles;
gaining commitment; planning

Completion
"What did we do?"
Reviewing progress; understanding
the past; moving on

Below are descriptions of each of the five conversations, with a summary of the behaviour we may see if its missing. If you are having trouble with another individual or group (you may want to return to your relationship map at the beginning of this chapter) then look at the behaviours you are finding difficult and decide if you can match this to a missing conversation. If you can, use the prompts in the model to help you have the conversation.

Relatedness conversations

Getting to know other people's point of view, understanding their position, agreeing what's important. If this conversation is missing, we tend to avoid the other party and view them as "other". The behaviours this engenders tend to be ones of avoidance and hostility. The surgeons mentioned above were in this position. We all know that if we don't feel connected to another person we will tend to avoid them, or at least avoid eye contact, until we have developed some sort of rapport. The fact that, in this model, relatedness comes first supports the view that authenticity is the foundation of all good leadership.

Exploration conversations

Developing options by generating new ideas and agreeing what is possible.
Once related, we can explore what is possible. If this conversation is missing, we tend to try to return to this point, reining back progress, in order to have our say. We tend to denigrate others as being foolish or stupid for not considering our point of view. Feeling like we haven't been heard makes us stubborn. I once worked on a project where the finance director had been on holiday when a crucial project meeting had taken place. He spent the next few months trying to undermine our efforts. We made no progress until we held a duplicate meeting, which he attended.

Decision conversations

Agreeing the way forward, making choices, closing down the options. Once we have a series of options on the table, we now need to close down the situation and make some decisions, reducing what we *could* do to what we *should* do. If this conversation is missing, then we are adrift forever in a world of possibility. Options abound, but nothing is fixed. In this case, we tend to find a lack of teamwork and alignment. People pull in different directions, often creating more conflict. Work grinds to a halt and everyone becomes disenchanted. I have had the misfortune to work on projects where we spent months planning different options, presenting them to the board and then reworking them. While no decisions were made, no progress was made either.

Action conversations

Agreeing who will do what and by when. We have made some decisions about what *should* happen. Only now can we decide *how* it's going to happen. If this conversation is missing, then, despite our good intentions, nothing gets done. Mostly we now spend time explaining away this lack of progress. I spent most of the Active chapter explaining why this is important. I won't repeat myself here.

Completion conversations

Agreeing "how that went", what can be learned, what we might do differently. We are now near the end. We have, we hope, agreed on who is going to do what. Now we need to look back and agree on what went well and what went badly. If we miss out this step, which is very common, we can easily view the past as negative, incomplete and therefore unsatisfying.

Many projects – and meetings – can peter out, leaving contributors feeling unsatisfied. I recommend the meeting effectiveness checklist as a good way of rectifying this. End-of-project meetings and reports are equally important.

The behaviours just described are shown on the right hand column of the model. On the left, it provides some examples of how we might use enquiry, acknowledgement and advocacy to prompt each conversation.

The point of this model is to emphasise that when facilitating, we must spot missing conversations and ensure that we return to a position where those conversations can be had before moving on. As suggested in the examples, the model can be used to steer conversations at different stages of a project. It can also be used to manage a single team meeting.

However you use it, the message is simple. If you see a group that is storming – disagreeing, displaying unhelpful team behaviour – ask yourself this: which conversation is missing and for whom, and how do I ensure that we return to have those missing conversations?

EXERCISE 20: FIND A MISSING CONVERSATION

Think about a team that you feel may be storming. Identify all the individuals that may be behaving in ways that suggest "conflict" within the group. Ask yourself what may be "missing" for the individuals in question by trying to match their behaviour to the left-hand column of the model. How do you invite them – and the rest of the team – to have that conversation together? Which forum? How long might they need? How do we ensure full attendance, and full attention? What help might we need to make it work?

COACHING: SAVE YOURSELF FROM SLEEPY HOLLOW

"Personally, I'm always ready to learn, although I do not always like being taught."

– WINSTON CHURCHILL

Let me ask you a question: what is the quickest and most powerful method of changing someone's mind? I'll return to this shortly with my own answer.

In the meantime, let us return to our team, which we hope has now been successfully facilitated through a period of storming. Tuckman's model now suggests it is ready to settle into a period of group cohesion. In other words, the group learns to work together. Behaviours settle, ways of working are agreed. Work gets done. The team is, to use the rather ugly term, *norming*. This period is not necessarily highly effective. If it continues for too long, without much progress or improvement it will result in a sense of tedium and lethargy. The team risks falling into what one of my friends calls Sleepy Hollow. This is a place of deep inertia, where individuals do their job from nine-to-five (or ten-to-four if they can get away with it). It is a place of quiet. A place where gonks adorn the computer screens and conversations are about children, soap operas and office gossip. In Sleepy Hollow, everyone has their role. And if someone is on holiday, that role simply doesn't get done.

What is needed, in order to prevent this regrettable decline, is to improve the performance of the individuals in the team. The team members need to be inspired to do better, to own the problems of the team as a whole. And this requires the leader to learn the important art of coaching.

Much – some might say too much – has been written about coaching and I won't add to the literature here save only to emphasise that coaching is a way of interacting with other people in order to help them learn for themselves. Often we can become stuck in our view of what is possible, what our role should be, how things should be done.[82] Coaching helps team members to see the world differently and therefore approach it differently. The trouble with coaching, as our model of team development clearly shows, is that it is hugely time consuming.

As a healthcare leader, it is likely that you have more skills and more experience than your team members. Your temptation will be to direct, using a didactic approach to problem solving, teaching and telling your team members what to do. There is, of course, an element of teaching in any leadership role. But teaching will not boost your team's performance. What you want from your team is innovation, resourcefulness, initiative. The very opposite of the qualities found in Sleepy Hollow.

What your team members need from you is something that will help them perform better *for themselves*. No-one, including Winston Churchill, likes to be told. They would prefer to work it out for themselves. Coaching works to encourage that to happen. So what is coaching? How does it differ from teaching or directing? Coaching involves changing the minds – or perhaps I should say the mindset – of the people in your team. And how do you do this? The answer is by asking Powerful Questions.

Powerful Questions

Powerful Questions open the mind to other possibilities. Powerful Question start with such phrases as: "What's your view on ...? Or "How do you think ... ?" Powerful Question invite the listener to explore their own views, approach and thinking. Powerful Question don't start with "Why?", which closes down the answer and invites "blame reasoning". Powerful Question explore and unearth the assumptions, beliefs, concerns and difficulties of a team member. Powerful Question build on each other, developing themes and avenues perhaps unanticipated by the questioner. Powerful Question are authentic, posed in a spirit of genuine enquiry.

When and how do you get a chance to formulate and ask these powerful questions? In many circles, coaching has a bad name. In my experience this means that offering anyone a coaching session is likely to be resisted. It is probably better to use more informal terms such as "one-to-ones" or "catch up sessions". Shorter, regular sessions are usually better, but if an individual is really struggling, it may be necessary to set aside a larger chunk of time. This is not psychoanalysis or psychotherapy. I am not encouraging your coaching sessions to explore subjects outside the work environment. I am merely encouraging you to help your team members think through their assumptions about their work and their role. Leading questions, and those designed to elicit a specific answer, are easily spotted as disingenuous and will have the opposite effect of what is intended. Coaching is a time set aside for the coach and team member to work together for the benefit of the team. [83]

So how often should you be doing this? My personal view is that if you are not offering every member of your team at least an hour of one-to-one time on a weekly basis then you risk your team sliding back into a period of storming, or – perhaps worse – drifting into Sleepy Hollow. Every week? I hear you cry. Now you understand the arrow on the Stages of Team Development model that says *Dependency*. It's a lot of time. At least a day – or possibly two – every week. But what would you prefer? More storming? Or Sleepy Hollow?

Coaching often needs to be done gently, and sometimes very gradually, as you gain the confidence of the team members and as they begin to see the world in a different way. But the benefits are huge. Not only will you occasionally, witness an "Aha!" moment – an almost tangible moment of epiphany, when an unhelpful way of thinking falls away – but you will slowly pave the way to the final stage when dependency drops away and performance takes off. There is no doubt that coaching is time consuming. It's a pure Golden Quadrant activity and for that reason it is often ignored or rushed. The temptation is instead to revert to setting direction or teaching. In other words, dictating your own answers rather than encouraging their formation in the mind of the team members. Sadly, this will make matters worse. More storming, team members leaving (remember, they'll be leaving you, not their job), disruption as new members join. Plummeting performance. More frustration. More late nights. Instead, learn to coach. The outcome is much better.

How do you know what questions to ask? How do you formulate these Powerful Questions? My answer is to return to the Missing Conversations model just described and study the left hand column. Use these cues and the five conversations as a structure for your coaching interactions. Remember to enquire, acknowledge and then advocate. Seek first to understand. Become more related: find out what is important to them, what their assumptions are, and what they understand of the situation you are discussing. Then tease out some options: what have they considered, what else they could do. You can prompt at this stage with some suggestions, but "learn to be wrong" about anything you suggest. This is probably the most important part of any coaching session: expanding the horizon. The Heath brothers' more recent book on decision-making (*Decide*) suggests that if we are stuck in an "either/or" question, we are probably not looking widely enough. The "Exploration" element of a coaching conversation can help widen the view and increase the available options. Only then should you spend some time honing the options down to one or two that can be pursued into the "action" conversation. Complete any coaching session by asking "How did that go?" Remember at all stages to use open and powerful questions.

This is simply my own very brief description of the coaching process based on my experience. There is a vast literature and substantial industry devoted to the subject and I don't pretend to have any special expertise.

What I have found, however, is that it's not a difficult skill to acquire, providing a spirit of authentic enquiry is maintained, and that your own ideas are kept to a minimum. I can guarantee that done well, coaching has transformative power. You'll be amazed by the results.

EXERCISE 21: SPEND TIME ONE-TO-ONE

Consider the group of people with whom you work most closely as a leader. This may be the group of people who formally "report to you" but may be more informal. Ask yourself if there is one person who would welcome some help with an issue. This is not something that they don't *know* but something that they may be struggling to begin, or to complete. Ask them if they would like to "talk it through" (I'd avoid specifically offering "coaching", it can appear patronising). Offer them some of your time to help. If they accept, spend the time questioning their understanding of the situation, where they might need help. Consciously focus on the style of your questioning, concentrating on open questions to help unpick why they are having trouble. Avoid offering concrete suggestions of your own. You may find it useful to read up on coaching or to get some training or help of your own before doing this.

Use the "Five Conversations" model to structure the conversation – remembering to include some completion questions at the end, asking how they feel and whether the session was useful.

Repeat.

DELEGATION: PUMP YOUR GOLDEN QUADRANT

Having now spent so much time and effort honing the skills of your team members, the final team leadership skill is one of letting go. As teams become more capable, performance increases, dependency decreases and the leader needs to be less in evidence. In Tuckman's model this phase is described as functional role relatedness or, more digestibly, *Performing*. Here, members work together to modify their own roles to complete the work at hand, they innovate and support each other. They are, to use a phrase, buzzing.

If you have ever had the good fortune to work in such a team, you will remember what it feels like. Exhilarating may be too strong a word, unless you are a member of an aeronautical display team,[84] but it certainly feels good to be part of a group of people who can be relied upon to perform, take up the slack, notice what is happening across the whole group, constructively engage and critique each other's work, innovate and change in response to challenges. At this stage, too much interference by a leader, especially a new leader, can have a detrimental effect – rapidly reverting them to the storming stage. Standing back and letting the team perform is what is required. And that skill has a name: delegation.

Most leaders I speak to fear delegation, often for good reason. If you delegate to a team, or a member of a team, which does not have the capability or capacity to do the task, the results will fall short of the standards you may expect. This is why coaching comes before delegation. The good thing, the light at the end of the tunnel, is the fact that delegation generates vast amounts of Golden Quadrant time. You need to eke out as much Golden Quadrant time and invest it in coaching in order to get there, but once you have, vast acres of time will open out. At the risk of repetition, I'll say that if you don't manage to find the time to coach your team out of the norming phase, then you'll never get your team to the performing stage. If you're struggling to see how that is possible, you may benefit from returning to the Active chapter and look carefully at how to generate more Golden Quadrant time.

The question is, as you approach this stage, what to delegate. The team does not simply arrive one day at a point of high performance, ready and waiting for all tasks to be delegated. Likewise at any one time, there are some tasks that can be delegated, and some that cannot, depending on the capability of the team members available. It is at this intersection between the individual and the task where the decision lies.

What I suggest is that you use the following model – based on the "skill-will" matrix popularised by the author Max Landsberg in his book *The Tao of Coaching*. Rather than using the more popular terms skill and will, I use the words "Competence" and "Commitment" – words that in my view have a slightly richer meaning. Competence is frequently measured in a healthcare setting and so can be tested. Commitment is a subject that we have covered extensively in an earlier chapter. The question that you must ask – before using this model – is this: For this particular individual, for this particular task, how competent and how committed are they?

FIGURE 12: Competence *vs* commitment

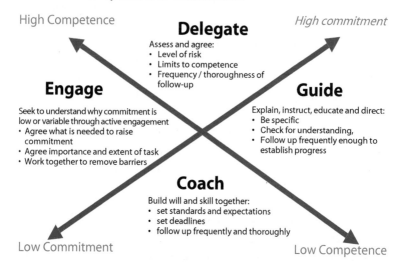

High Competence   **Delegate**   *High commitment*

Assess and agree:
• Level of risk
• Limits to competence
• Frequency / thoroughness of follow-up

Engage

Seek to understand why commitment is low or variable through active engagement
• Agree what is needed to raise commitment
• Agree importance and extent of task
• Work together to remove barriers

Guide

Explain, instruct, educate and direct:
• Be specific
• Check for understanding,
• Follow up frequently enough to establish progress

Coach

Build will and skill together:
• set standards and expectations
• set deadlines
• follow up frequently and thoroughly

Low Commitment   Low Competence

You may need to explore both aspects of this question by asking the individual. Commitment is not simply "willingness" – it incorporates both their level of confidence in their abilities and the time available, as well as their understanding of why the task should be done. It includes many other elements of context, such as whether they have a lot of other things on their plate or if this task will contradict or interfere with something else that they are doing. Similarly, competence may also not simply be a question of skill, but may also involve the level of support they may need from you and others.

When you have decided how much commitment and competence the individual has for this particular task, the model advises whether or not you should delegate. If they have both, in sufficient quantity, then you can delegate. You will need to ensure that you agree, as part of your act of delegation, how much risk you are willing to take and therefore how complete the task will need to be before you follow up. The frequency and extent of follow up will depend on your appetite for risk and your confidence in their levels of competence and commitment.

The model also allows you to consider how to deal with situations where either, or both, competence and/or commitment are missing. If competence is low, then a degree of instruction or other guidance will be necessary. If commitment is low, then you'll need to work on improving that – working out what the barriers are and helping to remove them. If both commitment and competence are low, then we're back to coaching, working out how to improve performance through a mixture of competence-building and engagement.

EXERCISE 22: DELEGATE ONE TASK

Consider one task that you would normally do yourself, but would prefer to delegate – perhaps to free up some time for another Golden Quadrant activity.

Identify one of your team who you feel may have sufficient commitment and competence to complete the task, albeit with supervision. Spend some time, one-to-one, with that person and discuss, using open questions:

1. Whether they would be interested in completing this for you. Ask if they have the time and resources.
2. Whether they are capable of doing it. Ask what their approach would be (don't tell – this is delegation, not instruction). Get a clear understanding of how they would do this.

If you're still convinced that they have both commitment and competence, ask them to complete this task. Agree, in advance, the point at which you will follow-up. Will this be when complete, or at some earlier stage? Agree what they will do if they meet barriers or problems. Agree to a time limit for completion.

Consider how this exercise differs from your normal style of delegation.

DISTINGUISH GETTING FROM BEING

Before I finish this chapter, I would like to offer one final concept and exercise that may help link the initial discussion about authenticity with the rather more practical skills I have just covered. It also links closely to the concepts we will cover in the next chapter on Focus.

The default understanding of the way the world works is that "What I have" influences "What I do" and that, in effect, determines "How I am". For example: *if we had more staff, my area would be easier to manage and so I would be less stressed.*

Sound familiar?

What happens, however, when we reverse these causal links? To what extent does "How I am" influence "What I do" (and therefore what other people around me do) and therefore "What I have"? (*if I was less stressed, my area would be easier to manage and so we would have more staff*).

Does this work? Is it possible that how you are as a leader influences those around you sufficiently to create an environment which you then blame for how you are? Is a stressed out environment likely to have more problems with staffing? It's likely, is it not?

So, aside from being authentic, how are you otherwise? To find out, let me suggest that you complete the exercise below.

I have found this exercise particularly powerful as the overall structure for a coaching session. If you do this, make sure that you establish enough context beforehand and gain permission from the person you are coaching to explore this in depth. You may also use this as an outline when you ask someone to coach *you* through a problem.

In summary, this chapter has been about the skills you can develop in order to engender the requisite energy in those around you. Working with authenticity you can develop your team through setting direction, facilitation, coaching and delegation. You can then use the idea of how you are *being*, in order to modify your approach to the challenges that will inevitably arise.

This follows on to the challenge that will exercise you more than any other, and for which you will need all the skills and capabilities you have developed hitherto. That problem is negativity.

EXERCISE 23: HAVING, DOING, BEING

Take a blank sheet of paper and spend some time working through these questions in the order given. I suggest taking it slow and spending about 5–10 minutes on each question. Before you start:

- List all of the things at work (projects, relationships, activities) that are going well for you.
- List all of the things at work (projects, relationships, activities) with which you are struggling.
- Select one of these issues as your topic. This is the issue that you are now working on for this exercise.
- Write down in two columns everything you can think of that you **have**, or **have not**, in relation to this issue. What assets have you got, what deficits are there?
- Write down everything that you are **doing** or **not doing** in relation to this issue. What are you trying to do, what are you avoiding?
- Write down a list of the adjectives that describe how you are **being** or **not being** in relation to this issue. How might other people describe your attitude or approach? What does it feel like when you contemplate this issue? Concentrate on the adjectives that describe how you are **not being** and select the three that have most resonance for you.
- Now construct a sentence, where the first three gaps are your chosen adjectives and the final gap is a description of your issue.
  "I am creating the possibility of being _____, _____, _____ in relation to _____."

This exercise offers you the opportunity to unearth the way that you are being in relation to a problem. Is this commonly the way you approach such issues? The exercise, at the end, asks you to consider a new way of being in relation to this problem. Having completed the exercise, you may find it helpful for you put this away for 24 hours and then review your answers.

FOCUSED
Tackle Negativity

They are playing a game. They are
playing at not playing a game.

– R D Laing, *Knots*

A few years ago, I worked in a hospital where, it was alleged, a member of staff was injecting intravenous saline – i.e. water – instead of prescribed medications. The member of staff freely admitted doing this, saying they thought placebo worked better than the medicines that had been prescribed. This dangerous violation was in no way out of character. In fact, this member of staff was well renowned for being difficult, with challenging behaviour and negative attitudes towards work and colleagues. When this transgression came to light, the staff member was suspended immediately from all duties, pending an investigation. Other members of staff hoped for a finding of gross misconduct which would lead to immediate dismissal. At last, they thought, we will finally be rid of this bad apple. Unfortunately, the organisation failed to adhere exactly to some HR processes. The union became involved. Accusations were made of bullying and victimisation and the situation became too difficult to pursue. The investigation was dropped and the staff member returned to work some weeks later, and no more was said. As a result, several people, including at least one high-performing leader resigned, unable to work in a place where it was possible to permit this level of misconduct without sanction.

WORKING LIFE FACTS

I tell this story because it highlights two really important facts about working life.

FACT 1: There are people whose attitudes and behaviours destroy the goodwill of those around them

At the risk of abandoning the positivity which I have advocated so strongly throughout this book, I call these people Negatives (with a capital N). You know who they are. When you come to work in the morning and they are on shift, your heart sinks. In any one area, you can usually count them one hand. But that doesn't make their existence a small problem. In my experience, they constitute about ten per cent of the workforce yet they cause more problems with HR and their team leaders than all the other staff put together. They eat up Golden Quadrant time like monsters, leaving you with less of your precious leadership time to spend on other members of staff who should have an equal call on your time. Negatives destroy or undermine all the Commitment, Action, Responsiveness and, above all, the Energy that you try to create.

Negativity may not always be as serious as the example of drug maladministration given above. But it is also not an isolated incident which makes for negativity. None of us are saints and we're all prone to occasional bouts of negativity. What distinguishes Negatives is how their complaints are, vicious gossip, jealousy, undermining, or simple unwillingness to co-operate, let alone go the extra mile.[85] The overriding problem is that they concentrate, for the most part, on things that detract from the job at hand. In many cases they can be technically adept, even excellent. But on the whole they are just too focused on themselves to really care for patients.

For balance, I should stress that about 20 per cent of your workforce are likely to be Positives. They are the people for whom you are thankful when they are on duty. They take the strain, they are happy and industrious. They volunteer, they smile, they deliver. And the remaining 70 to 75 per cent of the workforce are the Neutrals – the lumpen middle. They are easily influenced by those around them, often more strongly by the Negatives. As a result, Neutrals can turn negative.

FACT 2: If the percentage of negatives rises, teams and organisations can become dysfunctional

When negativity starts to rise, promoted and fuelled by Negatives, Neutrals will themselves become more negative. Previously easy-going team members will become more difficult and more demanding. Discretionary effort evaporates and so performance drops.

I once worked with a maternity unit that had recently emerged from such a period of dysfunction. It took the death of a baby to turn them around.[86] An investigation clearly showed that the mother had not asked for help with her sick baby because she overheard negative comments from midwives about patients' use of the call bell. Routine observations had not been done because, as the unit had become more dysfunctional, the important, routine stuff had been forgotten. When the baby was eventually found to be unwell, it was too late. The mother's eloquent testimony about her harrowing experience was captured on video by the investigating team and this terrible indictment was shown to all staff. It was this video that "found the feeling" necessary for the midwives to change their attitude.

Negativity – when it gets out of control – can be deadly. But there is good news. There is a solution to negativity and dysfunction.

FACT 3: Negatives can be challenged successfully

When challenged Negatives will do one of three things. About one third will step up, change their behaviour and may, in time, channel their energy to become positives. Another third, if put under any consistent level of pressure, will simply leave. And a final third – like in the first story about drug maladministration – will dig their heels in and use every technique in the book to get back at you. These Negatives will have fought their corner before and are liable to make mincemeat of any leader – especially a new leader – who is not prepared for this. If you're unlucky they will take you personally to the cleaners. Irrespective of their industry every leader with whom I have discussed this topic agrees: dealing with Negatives is the hardest thing they ever have to do. But it is probably also the most important. Because without challenge, Negatives can destroy you, your good work and put your patients at risk.

As evidence that successful challenge is possible I can do no better than point to a recent UK national survey of maternity services, which showed this dysfunctional department scored the largest positive swing in parental opinion ever recorded on a national survey and put it in the top ten per cent of places to have your baby in the UK. Negativity, when properly controlled, allows positivity to thrive and improves performance out of all proportion to the numbers of people involved.

Which is why this chapter is necessary. Its purpose is to equip you with some of the important skills and some practical ideas that may help you deal with Negatives, and thereby reduce negativity and promote the positivity that we all crave in our working lives. The first part is about defining positive behaviour by developing behavioural guidelines. The second talks about the games that Negatives play. We then describe some assertiveness techniques that will help you undermine such games. Finally, I suggest a way in which you can work on yourself to put yourself in a better position to manage these challenges. I sincerely hope that by using these ideas we can all help reduce negativity, and ensure everyone can focus on caring for patients.

EXERCISE 24: LOCATE YOUR NEGATIVES

Return to your Relationship Map from Exercise 17.

Look at the people that you have deemed to be "irregular" or "spiky" in shape. What are the reasons for this? Can you categorise these people as Negatives? To answer this ask yourself whether your view is shared by others – or is the challenging nature of your relationship just between the two of you.

You may also like to list the names of all the people you lead. Try to categorise them as Positives, Negatives or Neutrals. What is your percentage of Negatives?

AGREE ON YOUR BEHAVIOURAL NORMS

The worst year in the UK for road fatalities was 1966. That year we killed 8,300 people. Nearly 50 years later, in 2013, we killed or seriously injured only 1,713. While a bus-load of deaths each week is still far too many, we should remember that in that time, the number of vehicle miles has increased threefold. Taking these two statistics together, this is a 93 per cent reduction in serious road injuries and fatalities per vehicle mile.[87] Today, on average, you would have to drive the equivalent of 7,000 times round the equator before you have a collision where someone is

---

killed or seriously injured.[88] Death and serious injury on the UK's roads is becoming vanishingly rare.

What has made this possible? Clearly car technology is light-years ahead of where it was in 1966. Licensing has become tougher and roads are better. But what has changed, in my view, more than all of these, is the pressure we exert through the moral certainty of other drivers.

If you don't believe me, try getting drunk with friends and then picking up your car keys. Many will physically restrain you. Try driving the wrong direction up a one-way street. Or, less dramatically, just cheat a bit on the little white arrows in a supermarket car park. You'll soon find yourself the subject of significant remonstrations. Although the law is there, driving correctly is something that drivers also police for themselves.

This level of moral certainty is made possible through a simple device: The Highway Code. This little book, given to every learner at the beginning of their driving career, is beautifully simple. Running to a few tens of pages with plenty of diagrams it lists 307 rules of the road. Each rule is no more than a paragraph, sometimes just one short sentence. The Highway Code is not itself the law. It summarises the law using the words MUST and MUST NOT. But the majority of rules are not phrased like that. Instead, they tell drivers what they SHOULD or SHOULD NOT do in certain situations. You should, for instance, look both ways and listen before using an open railway crossing (Rule 298). It's hard to disagree with that – but also hard to legislate. The Highway Code builds a bridge between everyday common sense and the law.

In healthcare, we have a lot of law. We have the legal frameworks surrounding our professional registrations. We have laws managing almost everything that goes on in hospitals and clinics. As a doctor I am also bound by professional standards laid out in Good Medical Practice.[89] And we are also awash with policies and standard operating procedures (of which I will talk more in the Uniform chapter). Add to that, most organisations also have a code of conduct which provides rules that apply to all staff – often including such mundane matters as uniforms, nail polish and length of hair. We certainly have enough law.

But what is often missing is a set of rules that govern the day-to-day conduct of staff on the shop floor, something like the Highway Code, that would link these laws with common sense and give us a basis for the moral certainty necessary for us to police ourselves. This lack may be partly because the circumstances of healthcare differ more than those on the road. Anaesthetic rooms, outpatient departments and medical wards may all require subtly different rules. What's more, different departments have different histories and different cultures, that may require a different emphasis. It is my view that each network, each department, each area of responsibility, can benefit from its own set of behavioural guidelines, it's own Highway Code.

You may object. Surely we don't need another set of guidelines, or policies. We have enough such documents. I agree. We do. What I am advocating, however, is a document that is different in one important respect. It must be developed and agreed by the people to whom it applies. In my experience, it is only behavioural guidelines that are developed ground up that can gain real ownership. With them we can make specific the offences that we often find so difficult to control in Negatives. For instance, such rules will often contain things that say "Make an effort to be friendly and helpful, especially when things get busy or stressful". Like Rule 298, this sounds sensible. The point is, this is rarely, if ever, written down in the law, for the same reasons. It's hard to legislate through policies, SOPs or other documents. However, if you have developed such a set of behavioural guidelines, you and your team have a local highway code that will allow everyone to hold your Negatives to account.

Finally, you may also object that this sounds time-consuming and bureaucratic. Not so. The way that I create these with teams requires no more than an hour in a process which I call "Good Day Bad Day".

GOOD DAY BAD DAY

To do this, I recommend taking a selection of staff into a room for between 45 minutes and an hour and playing the Good Day Bad Day game. Label three sheets of paper, preferably flip-charts, as follows: "What happens?", "What do you see?" and "What do you hear?". Under each label, divide the paper vertically into two columns with the headings "Good Day" and "Bad Day". First ask the attendees to fill in the three columns marked "Bad Day". Start with "What happens?". Ask your colleagues to describe the worst possible day in terms of the events that can happen. This usually involves staff calling in sick, inadequate equipment, too many patients and so on, but with a little prompting can also include a bit of fun: major incidents, visits from royalty .... Then ask them to describe, under "What do you see?", the kind of behaviour they might see on a bad day, given the worst possible cases of staff behaviour. List some typically bad things that people do. The list usually starts with "Coming back late from breaks" and "Storming off in a huff" and then burgeons from there. Third, list out some words and phrases under "What do you hear?". This should include things that people say when they're having a bad day – things you really don't want to hear. Some of these will be unprintable, but many will be about avoiding work, blaming other people, or just being rude.

Once you've done those three columns, which takes about 15 to 20 minutes, start again, this time filling in the missing columns: first, what happens on a good day, then describe how people behave on a good day and finally, what sort of things do you hear people say on a good day. This takes another 15 to 20 minutes. I tend to encourage participation by splitting any group larger than six into smaller huddles and have them report back and describe what they have written. This may take a little longer, but it means more people speak.

The exercise can be a bit of fun, and it finishes on a positive note. With a bit of context setting at the beginning and a few words to wrap up at the end, the whole thing takes less than an hour. You can run it with any number of people. In the past I've done multiple sessions capturing people as they are free for breaks or lunch and so managed to include everyone in a large department in less than half a day.

When you have finished the exercise, you need to write this up. First, ignore the columns about the bad day. Concentrate instead on the column of good behaviour under "What do you see?" on a good day. These comments become your behavioural guidelines. You can also develop "Do Say Don't Say" guidelines about specific phrases that you should or should not hear. To keep these positive, focus mainly on the "Do Says" which you'll find under "What do you hear?" on a good day.

With these Behavioural Guidelines and Do Say Don't Say Guidelines, suitably spruced up and published, you have a bespoke set of rules, which, providing you have included everyone in the exercise, are already agreed.[90] No further consultation or communication is required. Just print and distribute. The inclusive nature of this very simple exercise makes the output much more powerful than anything that could be designed in committee or, indeed, in law.

EXERCISE 25: DEVELOP SOME BEHAVIOURAL GUIDELINES

At your next team meeting, whether for your leadership challenge, or those you manage directly, run through the Good Day Bad Day exercise described above. Write-up and distribute the resulting Behavioural Guidelines.

You now have a set of behavioural guidelines which you and your team can use to hold people to account for negative behaviour. Perhaps one of your Negatives is persistently late for work. If one of your behavioural rules is "Be on time", then everyone can use this rule as evidence that this is unacceptable. Self policing now becomes possible.

SPOT THE GAMES

Self policing won't be enough. You will also need to confront and challenge negative behaviour yourself. This is difficult, for two reasons. First, it involves conflict, and few people are immune to the anxiety this induces. Secondly, it probably involves challenging a Negative. And the Negative has two advantages: the first advantage is their armoury of techniques of emotional manipulation, most of which they have learned from childhood. Their second advantage is that they've done this before. Probably many times. They've likely had plenty of practice wriggling out of such confrontations while you, by contrast, may never have done this before. I'll repeat what I said earlier: according to all the leaders I have asked, this is the most difficult aspect of being a leader.

To help you, I'm going to introduce the concept of Transactional Analysis. In 1964 Eric Berne, a Canadian-born psychoanalyst, published a book that was intended for fellow professionals, but which rapidly became a worldwide bestseller. *Games People Play* shed light on this previously arcane aspect of psychotherapy. Its jargon-free style and the large number of practical examples makes it accessible to the lay reader even today. It remains a very usable manual.

The essence of transactional analysis is that when we spend time with others we structure and craft our social interactions with precision, albeit unconsciously. These transactions may occur in overtly social occasions such as parties or going to the pub, but will also take place during any social interaction at work. What we say in the coffee room – our discussion of football teams, shopping habits, or our views on our organisation and our colleagues – are psycho-social transactions. We are trading positions on subjects, and the positions we take often have an underlying meaning distinct from the content. Importantly, this is also true for the more formal conversations we have. Handing over or reviewing a patient on a ward round may not sound like a "psycho-social transaction", but it is. The way we conduct ourselves, how we address each other, and the assumptions we make about the positions or standing of different people, makes it social as much as professional.

As an example, consider this. The setting is a ward, where a senior doctor is conducting (in every sense of the word) a ward round accompanied by the ward sister and a junior doctor:

Senior Doctor: *(aggressively leafing through the notes)*
Where are these patient's blood results?
Junior Doctor: They're not back yet. I can try to ring the lab.
Senior Doctor: That's hopeless! Where is this patient's named nurse? They should know!
Ward Sister: I don't think that is the nurse's responsibility.
Senior Doctor: *(raises eyes to heaven and mutters)* Probably on her break anyway. Everyone's always on a break – apart from me!
Ward Sister: We're understaffed as usual.
Senior Doctor: This place is hopeless.
Ward Sister: We're doing the best we can …
Senior Doctor: *(throws notes onto trolley)* Right! No X-Ray reports either. I'll be back when you're ready to do some work! *(storms off)*
… scene continues day-after-day, often for many years.

Transactional analysis asserts that in any such transaction the parties adopt one of three ego states: parent, adult or child. In parent mode we may direct, scold or mollify. In child mode we may become helpless, obstinate or demanding. In adult mode we are doing neither. We are engaging as equals.

Our best interests are served by adult to adult transactions. According to Berne, adult transactions allow us to develop autonomy, spontaneity and intimacy – or, couched the terms of this book, they allow us to generate positivity at work. Unfortunately, we all have some tendency towards parent–child interactions through habits learned over many years. When we get to know each other well, as we do in marriages, families or at work, transactional analysis suggest we can fall into habits of parent–child transactions. These habits can become ingrained into games. Berne defines games as:

> … an ongoing series of complementary ulterior transactions progressing to a well-defined, predictable outcome. Descriptively it is a recurring set of transactions, often repetitious, superficially plausible, with a concealed motivation; or, more colloquially, a series of moves with a snare or "gimmick". Games are clearly differentiated from procedures, rituals and pastimes by two chief characteristics: (1) their ulterior motive and (2) the payoff.

The scenario above, where the senior doctor becomes ever more enraged with his colleagues is very clearly a parent–child transaction. The doctor is the angry parent, and the other staff are wayward children. What may be less clear from such a short snippet is that this may, by Berne's definition, be a game. If this scene is repeated day after day, then the anger cannot be genuine – it is a move in a game. The doctor's ulterior motive is to maintain a power-base through fear and domination. The ulterior motivation of the ward sister is to irritate the doctor even further by spouting plausible platitudes or half-truths. The predictable outcome is the doctor losing control and the ward sister, presumably, having further reason to complain about the doctor. This behaviour creates distance between the players and therefore prevents intimacy in an environment that can be emotionally threatening – i.e. a ward filled with sick people. The pay off for everyone, is that by playing this game no-one has to face the patients' suffering.

Not all games may be so obvious, but if you look for them, they are often there. "The Management" – or the "Department of Health" or any other absent figure of authority can be used as distant parents, allowing everyone to be helpless in the face of a crisis. Distant parents can also provide permission for parent-like behaviour by leaders. I have been in a meeting, allegedly part of an investigation into a patient safety incident, where individuals have been grilled by senior leaders to the point of tears. The reasons for being so iron-fisted is, in my view, the fear of being investigated by a regulator, government department or commissioner.[91]

The alternative explanation is that it creates a pay off that avoids facing the true prevalence of avoidable harm.

What happens if such games become prevalent throughout an institution? The answer is probably best answered by the most famous ethnographic description of a transactional analysis, published a few years before *Games People Play*, by one of the founders of the Tavistock Institute, Isabel Menzies Lyth. In her ground-breaking monograph published in 1960, "Social Systems as a Defence Against Anxiety" Lyth describes an array of games and positions taken by trained and student nurses in order to distance themselves from the suffering of their patients. In one scenario, individuals tend to accuse their juniors of being irresponsible (i.e. childlike) and those more senior to them as being too strict (i.e. parental). Behaviour tended to flow from these generalisations. Despite many decades since its publication, it remains a sobering account of how we can use parent–child transactions to help us maintain hierarchy and distance within healthcare.

FOUR COMMON GAMES

Berne's book contains many games that reflect his practice as a psychotherapist and marriage guidance counsellor. In modern working life, many of his examples are not relevant (unless, of course, you're having a lot of unsatisfactory sex with your colleagues). Instead, I can suggest four games that I have most often seen played out. In these explanations, I've simplified the scenarios and used Red and White as the names of two players, to make it more readable.

You're wrong

White insists on being right, at the expense of Red – taking an argument to the point at which they have to admit defeat. Red tries to come back with more evidence. The argument becomes detailed, entailing long discussions about who is at fault. Eventually they "agree to disagree" but the argument simmers and occasionally comes back to the surface.

Do what I say

White tries to dominate Red (and often everyone else) at every opportunity. White wants to ensure that Red does everything to their orders. Red is often criticised for not doing things correctly and rework is ordered. Red tries to avoid being told what to do. Red and White complain about each other. White asserts that Red is incapable. Red asserts that White is a bully.

Red may go off sick, which both solves and perpetuates the game.

Let me explain
White's objective is justification of past events. Much time is spent explaining and describing what happened in the past, usually in laborious detail. White wants Red to understand everything, whether relevant or not. Red tries not to hear, and is therefore often absent from decision-making, which requires more explanation.

Zero sum
This is a three-handed game where White sets up a conflict between two others in such a way that it presents a win or lose situation to both: Red versus Red. Everyone colludes in the need to resolve a problem which is often trivial or irrelevant.

In all of these games, the pay off is avoiding the anxiety of dealing with patients and their feelings. By getting caught up in such internal conflicts and arguments, the patient is side-lined. These games tend also to increase the fear and fixation that undermine kindness towards patients and colleagues. The reduction in relatedness, the sapping of energy and creativity reduce the sense of positivity in an organisation.

SIX ASSERTIVENESS TECHNIQUES
The good news is that it is possible to undermine and remove such game-playing. In the dysfunctional maternity unit I described earlier there was a good deal of game-playing. The turnaround to positivity was effected by new leaders who refused to play the games and insisted on adult to adult conversations. In their case, they instituted a new organisational structure, which forced people to re-apply for their jobs. This very stringent process, where the interviews were conducted in a true adult–adult style, reconfigured the stage upon which the games were being played and removed many of the Negatives that were fuelling them.

Thankfully, you do not need to undertake an entire reorganisation to get a sizeable reduction in negative behaviour. Instead, you need to learn how to spot such games and refuse to play along with them. The simplest way to do this is to learn the gentle art of assertiveness. I would recommend *When I Say No I feel Guilty* to learn a theory of assertiveness. This 1975 bestseller by Manuel Smith, a Californian psychotherapist, has many clear examples and practical tips on how to manage manipulation – his term for playing games or negativity. He offers six simple verbal techniques of assertion – adult responses that will make any game crumble.

Broken record

Negative manipulation often involves diversion into other territory, deflecting from the current situation with story-telling, excuses or justification. Broken record simply means repeating what you want, without any embellishment. This makes your needs clear and unambiguous. Returning to your assertion time and time again – saying "I want" or "I need" and repeating this without any variation – brings us back to the present issue until it's resolved.

Fogging

Manipulation usually involves making statements intended to generate anger, resentment or fear and thereby create an argument off-topic. Fogging is unseating such negative comments by using agreement. This may be partial agreement, agreement with the odds or agreement in principle. If, in a discussion of time-keeping, someone tells you "You're not exactly punctual yourself" (inviting a rebuttal and thereby creating grounds for an argument about your own time-keeping, rather than theirs), you can say "Sometimes I am late" (partial agreement), "You may be right" (agreement with the odds) or "My time-keeping does need work" (agreement in principle) – each of which removes the possibility of further discussion.

Self Disclosure

Manipulation involves trying to create barriers and reduce relatedness. Offering free information about yourself and a personal account of what is happening for you stops this from happening. Self disclosure means saying "I feel" or "I too have experienced", but without any intention of apportioning responsibility for feelings to someone else. If self-disclosure is used wisely, and not used as a counter-manipulative strategy (e.g. by saying things like "you make me feel') then you generate the opportunity for relatedness in the face of aggression.

Negative assertion

One of the ways we can avoid being manipulated is to embrace our faults (we all have them, I'm told). By making it clear that you accept a critical view of yourself, you disarm the ability of any Negative to manipulate a situation. Whereas Fogging repeats manipulative comments as truth, Negative Assertion brings out your faults without encouragement. For instance, saying "I'm not good with numbers" prevents any manipulation based on your numeracy skills. It has to have some truth. If you're a maths whizz, such a comment is clearly counter manipulative.

Negative enquiry

Another response to negative comments can be to explore them, prompting more exacting criticism to reduce manipulation. Asking for more information about a negative comment without trying to counter or deny it can defuse it's power to undermine. If someone says "You're an idiot!" then asking authentically "What specifically do you find idiotic about me?" creates an adult space. It offers the opportunity to really understand. One tip: avoid asking "Why?". It sounds critical and invites confrontation.

Workable compromise

Finally, once all the negativity has been diffused we need to address the issue at hand. A workable compromise is the adult end point of any such interaction. This is where you invite the discussion on how and where you can agree.

To illustrate these six ideas, let's play-back the earlier scenario and imagine how our ward sister might use these assertiveness techniques with our senior doctor:

Senior Doctor:	What are these patient's blood results?
Junior Doctor:	They're not back yet, but I can try to ring the lab.
Senior Doctor:	That's hopeless! Where is this patient's named nurse? They should know!
Ward Sister:	The patient's named nurse is not here at the moment.
Senior Doctor:	*(raises eyes to heaven and mutters)* Probably on her break anyway. Everyone's always on a break – apart from me!
Ward Sister:	That's probably true (*FOGGING – agreeing with the odds*) but we need to finish the ward round. (*BROKEN RECORD*)
Senior Doctor:	I can't do the ward round if there are no results!
Ward Sister:	I agree that might be difficult (*FOGGING – PARTIAL AGREEMENT*) but we need to finish the ward round. (*BROKEN RECORD*)
Senior Doctor:	This place is a mess, I can't work in this environment

	any more.
Ward Sister:	I often feel the same way (*SELF DISCLOSURE*) but we need to finish the ward round (*BROKEN RECORD*).
Senior Doctor:	The nursing staff are never here when you need them!
Ward Sister:	I know (*FOGGING*). I get pretty annoyed about it too. (*SELF DISCLOSURE*) And I'm sure I'm often unavailable when I'm needed. (*NEGATIVE ASSERTION*) But we really need to finish the ward round. (*BROKEN RECORD*)
Senior Doctor:	This whole ward is hopeless!
Ward Sister:	What, specifically, do you find hopeless. (*NEGATIVE ENQUIRY*)
Senior Doctor:	The blood results are never available!
Ward Sister:	I'm sure we can find ways to improve that. (*WORKABLE COMPROMISE*) But right now we need to finish the ward round. (*BROKEN RECORD*)
Senior Doctor:	OK, but we really need to fix this. It's driving me crazy.
Ward Sister:	Let's have a meeting after the ward round to discuss what we need to change. (*WORKABLE COMPROMISE, BROKEN RECORD*)

Notice in this exchange that the ward sister does not engage in any of the prompts to enter into parent–child conversations, which are invited through the goading comments about uselessness of nurses or the ward. There is no attempt to enter into the four common games by (a) trying to prove the doctor wrong (*we always have the blood results, it's just this patient*), (b) trying to reverse dominate (*you're being unprofessional!*), (c) attempting to justify the situation (*the problem is with the lab …*) or (d) to set up a win/lose situation (*if you don't finish the ward round then I'll report you to …*). The assertiveness is cool, adult and clear. The game-playing doctor is left without someone to play with and eventually has to revert to adult behaviour.

I will add one small word of warning. Assertiveness without compassion and authenticity becomes aggression. For instance, simply repeating your demands endlessly without saying anything else – i.e. using Broken Record in isolation, without listening or responding to the other side – is clearly childish. Assertiveness is about reducing manipulation and negativity to create an adult, and eventually more positive, space. Use these techniques sparingly and wisely without trying to counter-manipulate.

EXERCISE 26: PLAYING AT GAMES

A fun exercise is to simulate situations that require assertiveness with one or two other people in order to practise your techniques. One person takes the role of game player – e.g. the senior doctor in the example above. Another then tries to diffuse their game – e.g. the ward sister in the example above. While the third person watches and takes notes. The situation and the roles should reflect the challenging situations that you face in your daily work. Having done this once, rotate the roles so that everyone has a chance to be difficult or challenging and to be assertiveness and keep the conversation adult. After each attempt, the note-taker can feed back what they thought went well and what could have been improved. It can be helpful if the note-taker can identify the point at which the six assertiveness techniques were used.

LOOK WITHIN

I hear another objection. You have re-read the new dialogue showing how the ward sister undermines the game-playing of the senior doctor. You are unconvinced. If you were the ward sister, you'd never be able to keep your cool like that. You would blow your top, shout back, sulk off, maybe ring the GMC … any response other than the neat-and-tidy responses suggested above. And for most people, this is true. If you hit the right buttons, you get the usual response. The senior doctor in this example – and all the Negatives in your organisation – have been pushing the right buttons for years.

How do we control ourselves in the face of negativity and manipulation? How do we create the mental space to formulate the oh-so-adult responses of Negative Enquiry, Fogging and so forth? It's not easy. Anyone who has been a parent, especially of teenagers, knows this. What can we do?

I have a suggestion – learn to meditate.

The experience of untold thousands of individuals from all walks of life (including me) and from all religions and none, supported by a vast amount of reliable research, is that a short daily meditation session will help set your mind on a path of peace, good health and compassion.[92] If you're in healthcare, that can't be a bad thing.

Meditation may sound esoteric or religious, but need not be. Meditation can be very straightforward and entirely secular. It is about creating time in your day to relax and study your mind. There are hundreds of meditation techniques[93] but the one most commonly taught in the West is mindfulness of breathing.[94] Such meditation techniques involving mindfulness have become the foundation for several recent movements, including the very successful, and widely studied Mindfulness Based Stress Reduction (MBSR) programme started by Jon Kabat-Zinn at the University of Massachusetts Medical Center. As Professor Emeritus of Medicine, he remains one of the foremost proponents of using mindfulness techniques in daily life – although he tends to refrain from calling it meditation.[95] There are untold books and articles on mindfulness and meditation. There is a year-long secular meditation course offered online at *headspace.com* and thousands of guided meditations available free at *insighttimer.com* – a community congregated around a meditation timer app. There are also Vipassana movements which emphasise the secular and scientific aspects of meditation, a notable one developed by the Burmese teacher S N Goenka who famously brought his brand of meditation to Indian prisons, with very positive effects.[96] And there is also the Transcendental Meditation (TM) movement which has many eloquent promoters, including the filmmaker David Lynch.[97]

I am not going to recommend or comment on any of these. Different styles and different methods suit different people. All I can do here is offer a very brief description, through the exercise below, of mindfulness of breathing. This should demonstrate how simple this is. You may have to take on trust the idea that doing this for ten minutes a day will transform your ability to deal with negativity. Yet it is true. You will likely discover, if you do this, that your levels of self awareness, and therefore your capacity to see yourself entering into negativity will increase. You'll start to see games for what they are, rather than be drawn into them. You will find a gentle distance builds up between you and the emotions you find difficult, which is very liberating. As a result, your levels of vitality will rise. You'll be healthier. And happier. Possibly very much happier.[98]

EXERCISE 27: WATCH YOUR BREATH

Find a quiet place. Sit comfortably, upright but not too erect, in a chair, with your eyes gently closed. Set a timer for ten minutes (egg timer, smartphone app, it doesn't matter). Ensure that you will have no interruptions.

During the ten minutes, focus your mind on your breathing. Watch your breath as it comes in and goes out. Do not try to change your breathing.

Your body knows how to breathe, so just watch it. When you find, inevitably, that you have lost your mindfulness and are thinking about something else, do two things. Smile gently to yourself (don't blame yourself, be thankful that you've noticed). Then note that you were thinking and gently bring yourself back to watching your breathing. Every time your mind wanders, bring it back.

The gentleness with which you return to your mindfulness of your breathing is very important. You are a caring professional. Be caring towards your mind. This is not a game where one part of your mind tries to dominate another. It is not a competition to see how little you can force your mind to wander. It is an exercise in self-awareness. In fact, the point when you notice that your mind has wandered is the most important part of the exercise, because it is there – in that moment of self-awareness – that you are looking directly at your mind. You notice what you are thinking, rather than merely thinking it.

When you realise your mind has wandered you can see, in sharp relief, where your mind has gone. This is the cutting-edge of self-awareness, so don't be cross. Be thankful. Just keep watching the breath, noticing – with care – that your mind has wandered and return to the breath. Do this, and this alone, for ten minutes.

For the purpose of this exercise, itches and urges to shift position are also types of thinking. If you can, just notice them and return to the breath. Notice them, return to the breath and very soon they will disappear.

Repeat this exercise daily or twice daily. If you find it useful and comfortable, you can also increase the length of the sessions.

UNIFORM
Control your processes

If you can't describe what you're doing as a process, you don't know what you're doing.

– W Edwards Deming

On 29 January 2009, the *New England Journal of Medicine* published a paper that demonstrated something unprecedented. It was a method of reducing the complications of surgery. The study showed how, over a period of just 12 months, the research team had managed to halve the death rate and reduce by more than 30 per cent the rate of major complications, including wrong site surgery. The eight hospitals in which this new treatment was tested were scattered across the world, in many different surgical environments from highly advanced to rudimentary. What made this report of a major international advance in surgical safety so remarkable was not just the extraordinary results the team had achieved, but the simplicity of the intervention they had discovered. They had introduced into the operating theatre a single piece of paper. What they were reporting was the results of the first trial of the now ubiquitous WHO surgical safety checklist.

The WHO checklist insists that the team doing an operation take just a few moments before putting knife to skin. During this brief check, everyone in the room agrees not just who is on the table and what operation is going to be performed but also what predictable complications might ensue. This 20-second chat, it turns out, reduces the risk of surgical mishap more than any other invention of the past 100 years. Subsequent studies have backed up the initial, ground-breaking study. As a result, the WHO checklist has, within just a few years, become mandatory in all surgical environments worldwide. Given the estimated 250 million surgical procedures undertaken across the globe every year, it is reasonable to assume that this simple innovation has already saved hundreds of thousands of lives.

The story and reasoning behind this deceptively simple device is told beautifully by its most famous advocate, the surgeon and WHO External Lead for the Safer Surgery Initiative, Atul Gawande, in his book *The Checklist Manifesto*.[99] He demonstrates how checklists, which are used extensively in many other industries including most famously in aviation, help to create a sense of teamwork, insist on communication at critical times[100] and ensure that slips, lapses and mistakes are minimised. Checklists, it transpires, if used well, are a very effective way of reducing active errors. His view – and mine – is that we should use them more extensively in healthcare.

However, this chapter is not exclusively about checklists, although, as we shall see, they form part of the story. It is about processes more generally. I hope by the end, you will see how useful it is to regard everything you do at work as being part of a process. Using a handful of simple rules, we will cover the three critical areas: communication, measurement and improvement.

PROCESSES ARE WHAT HAPPENS

Processes are easily defined. We simply say that a process is any series of agreed steps, designed to achieve a result or output. In this view of our organisation we construe our work as being like a production line. This is not to exclude the fact that there are other important qualities or metaphors that can describe our organisation – including, for instance, as a web of relationships.[101] However, at the very simplest level, healthcare consists of three steps: admit, treat, discharge. The result or output is, we hope, a healthier patient. Within each of these steps are myriad other, sub-steps. Each step can be further broken down into further sub-steps *ad infinitum*.

Thinking of work as being a process, or a production line, may sound tedious or uncaring, but this view is hugely important. If we are to treat our patients effectively, we need to do the right things, in the right order. As a result, everything we do as leaders comes eventually to this point, where we do something for our patients. Whatever the environment, everything we do that has any value is part of process that eventually changes something for the patient. Process is what happens.

Managed well, processes ensure that we get things right – first time and every time – for every patient. It is for this sense of repeatability – rather than any lack of personalisation – that I call this chapter Uniform.

By contrast, unimproved or badly managed processes will guarantee things go wrong for patients. For instance, I heard recently of a disastrous mistake in a laboratory where labels from two tissue samples from different hospitals were swapped by mistake and as a result, a patient with aggressive cancer was given the all-clear and a patient with a benign growth had a healthy organ removed. This is a tiny process error, with life-changing consequences. All healthcare related error is, at the point of execution, an example of wrong process.

ERRORS IN PROCESS

I started this chapter with a story about the brilliant success of the WHO surgical checklist for a reason. This story tells us something very important and also slightly daunting about processes in healthcare. This valuable and exceptional piece of work tells us that we are, for the most part, extremely bad – often negligently bad – at managing processes.

To explain why I say this, we should put the success of the WHO checklist into perspective. Every life saved and every error trapped by the surgical safety checklist – and there are millions of them to date – represents an error in a process. And this is not just any process. This is the surgical process. This is a critical, emotionally charged, highly important, very dangerous process. A process over which you would expect people to take considerable care and expend considerable effort assuring it is right. And yet even with the checklist in place, in as many as one per cent of cases, with the patient on the table, draped and ready, surgeon knife-in-hand, we discover (and thankfully correct) an error that could have put the patient's life at risk.

Let us ask ourselves what that would look like in other industries: one in every hundred new houses might fall and kill its occupants; one in every hundred smartphones might blow up in the face of its purchaser; one in every hundred cars driven from the production line could be a death trap; and one in every hundred aircraft might fall from the sky. The WHO checklist is a wonderful invention. It has reduced our rate of error in this critical process from about maybe 1 in 100 to 1 in 1000. This is commendable, but the context is not. In comparison to manufacturing processes – where the error companies are chasing often is substantially less than one in 3.4 million [102] – it is frankly terrible.

Part of the reason for this situation is that there has been a chronic underfunding of information technology (IT) in healthcare. [103] Without good IT, process control needs to be done manually and paperwork introduces substantial opportunities for error. The other significant contribution to healthcare's lag in process management is that, like bespoke tailoring, it requires high degrees of variation. Healthcare is a service industry which employs vast numbers of skilled and semi-skilled workers to patch together many smaller processes to create a larger individual process, each one of which is different for each patient. [104]

As an example, let us take my own speciality of Emergency Medicine. When a patient arrives in an emergency department, they may take one of several routes, traditionally called Minors, Majors or Resus, depending on the severity of their presentation. Within each of those areas, different activities are undertaken, depending on the patient's condition and their response to treatment: observations are taken, patients are examined, drugs are prescribed, investigations are ordered. At each point, staff members are taking a series of complex inter-related decisions and communicating them orally and in writing. If we were to map the journey of each patient, showing what activity had happened, they would each be different.

What's more, all of the individual activities are themselves dependent upon other processes in the hospital which ensure, for instance, that shelves are stocked, floors are cleaned, equipment is suitably serviced, and staff are trained. If we were to try to map all these processes in some huge diagram, showing all the dependencies and decisions that are taken at different stages, it would produce a vast and incomprehensible diagram.

This variation is why healthcare is prone to mistakes. Unlike a car or a smartphone – whose factories produce just a handful of models at any one time and where variation between individual products is limited to certain pre-defined options – we produce an entirely different product for every customer. What is amazing is that in this situation we make so few mistakes. Sidney Dekker, a specialist in disaster investigation and writer on the subject has pointed out, what keeps our patients safe in their beds is not robust systems, processes and policies that exist predefined in our environment. What keeps our patients safe is the skill, intelligence, motivation, and constant vigilance demonstrated by our staff.[105]

Which is where you come in.

You will be pleased to hear that mapping processes in laborious detail is not necessary or desirable. I am not even sure it's possible. You will certainly need to define your processes clearly and communicate them widely but you will need to do so intelligently, allowing the users to patch your process into the web of other processes that they are trying to effect. I will describe process block diagrams as a way of doing this. You will also need to change and improve your processes. For this you will need to measure their efficacy and efficiency and you will need to set up methods to review and change your processes. For this we will need checklists, measurement tools, and a management system which – you will be unsurprised to hear – will involve more decision-making meetings.

But all of this will be impossible unless you also do what the rest of this book has exhorted and create the environment and culture where staff are motivated and happy to manage this complex web of processes. Primarily, what is necessary is for you, as a healthcare leader, to maintain the skill, motivation and intelligence of your staff to manage these processes as best they can, given the enormous amount of variation. This is why this chapter comes so late in the CAREFUL approach. The principle is *people before process*. So, as a word of warning, if you haven't attempted the suggestions and exercises in the previous chapters, your success with the exercises and approaches to this chapter will likely be limited. Unhappy staff don't manage processes well.

FOUR PROCESS RULES

For simplicity, I've divided this chapter into four sections, each of which is headed by a simple rule that will, I hope, summarise the most important messages facts.

RULE 1: YOU OWN THE PROCESS

If you, as leader, have responsibly for a particular activity within a particular area of a hospital or clinic, then you *own* the process. The concept of *ownership* is a useful metaphor because it helps identify how you need to behave towards the process. Owners, as distinct from renters, look after their property. They expend time, energy and effort making sure that it's protected and maintained. They nurture it. They don't expect other people to do that, or blame others when it isn't done. Owners are attentive and proactive.

Let's take an example. If you're the Occupational Therapy (OT) manager for a particular area, then – contrary to what you may think – you are *not* responsible for how OT is delivered. That responsibility lies with your talented and much-loved therapists.[106] You are responsible for the *process*. And you are accountable (a distinction we will draw more fully in Rule 3). So you will need to nurture the process, expending time, energy and effort making sure that it is protected and maintained. When the OT process fails in some way then you will need to fix it.

For all that to happen, you need to communicate how OT works, measure its success or efficacy and take time improving it. Communication, measurement, improvement. The next three rules cover these aspects.

EXERCISE 28: WHAT PROCESS DO YOU OWN?

Return to your leadership challenge and ask yourself these questions:
- How does your leadership challenge translate into "process"?
- How do you currently describe or document this process?
- Which staff members are responsible for executing the process (this may be across several areas or departments)?
- How do you currently ensure that this process is understood and retained by these staff?
- How do you agree changes to the process?
- How do you communicate those changes?

RULE 2: PROCESSES ARE IN THE MINDS OF YOUR STAFF

Fully automated processes, like filling cereal boxes in a factory, are agreed in advance when the machinery is designed. In healthcare, we have few such automated processes. For the vast majority of the time we are providing service rather than product, so our processes need to be agreed by the humans performing the steps. This leads us to the inconvenient truth so fundamentally important to patient safety and to healthcare leadership – including your leadership – that it should be writ large on every office wall: *your processes are in the minds of your staff.*

The documentation – whatever form it takes – is not the process. It is what your staff *think* the documentation says that defines the process in reality. A policy or standard operating procedure (SOP) may be legally required, but it is only useful through its capacity to influence what is in the minds of your staff. What you, as leader intend has no relevance. A bold poster stuck to every door of your hospital may help, but the process is at all times in the minds of your staff. If your staff changes – which they do, every shift – and they have differing ideas of the process, then your process changes with every shift. The exact opposite of uniformity.

To make matters worse, as we have discussed in previous chapters, the fact that your staff know *what* they should do, does not guarantee that they will do it when you delegate it to them. The minds of your staff include not only their knowledge, but also their motivation.

Which means that every minute spent deciding your intended process (whether in consultation or typing on your computer) is completely wasted *unless* you then spend time absolutely ensuring, insisting and confirming that this is the process that exists in the mind of every single member of your staff. Doing this is a leadership activity, not a technical task. Hence, I will repeat: people before process.

Given how poorly process communication is done in most organisations, and the complexity of the processes we manage, it remains for me a source of continual amazement that any of our processes work at all. The fact that most hospitals and clinics do not fall apart is ample testament to the commitment and motivation of our staff.

I have three implications of this rule which are worth bearing in mind.

Corollary 1: If it's too complicated they won't remember it
Complicated SOPs and policies may be useful exercises in precision or legality, but they are often long and complicated documents. You are relying on everyone who executes or influences your process reading, remembering and acting on your policy. A summary may help, but often it's just more words. My view is that a Process Block Diagram (see below) can be helpful instead.

Corollary 2: If they can't find it, they'll make it up
Whatever means you use to summarise or communicate your process, it needs to be discoverable when things are busy. You are likely to have shared drives, or a policy management system, or other means of storing

collective information. But remember that many clinical staff can't easily access a computer while actually working – literally or metaphorically with their gloves on – so you'll need to find other ways to make your process visible. Antibiotic prescribing is part of a very complex, hospital-wide process. To help I've seen pharmacies use all means possible to ensure that people have the right information easily available for accurate prescribing: this has included – in one hospital alone – key-ring aides-memoire, brightly coloured booklets as well as easily accessible web-pages. If you're managing the OT process – or any other process – you can and should do the same.

A word of warning. You can send your process documentation or updates by email, but frankly, I wouldn't bother. Email makes no difference in the cut-and-thrust of clinical delivery, it fills up people's inboxes with what they will likely consider irrelevant, even if they do need to know. This will thereby actually reduce rather than increase their commitment. You'll need to be a bit more targeted, a little more subtle and – sorry to tell you – you'll need to take a lot more time engaging the staff you need to reach.

You should also bear in mind that this group of staff may include many more people than you first imagine. Because ...

Corollary 3: Processes fail at organisational boundaries

This consequence is less obvious than the previous two. Why does the fact that processes exist in the mind of your staff necessarily imply that processes will fail at organisational boundaries? The answer is that staff help each other. They remind each other and talk to each other about which processes exist and what they look like. In my own job, where I am responsible for delivering the first part of the patient-journey in my hospital, and where a huge number of processes intersect, I spend a lot of time checking and asking about how things work. How do we refer to Ophthalmology? Or Urology? How do we order a Malaria test? How does OT work on a Sunday? Most of the time I can find out by asking someone who has worked in my department longer than I have – or has a better memory. I don't know who the process owner is for any of these things – and they're probably not at work anyway – so I ask my immediate colleagues. When things go wrong, it's most likely because one group of people have failed to grasp another group's process, and they are not in the same room – or building – to check. So if, for instance, I leave a message on an answerphone in order to refer a patient to the OT department, thinking that is the correct process (actually, it's the process for Ophthalmology), and the message is not collected – the process has failed. This is the reason you need to communicate your process as widely as you possibly can, across all the organisational boundaries that you can imagine – getting into the nooks and crannies of the entire organisation.

Process Block Diagrams

One simple way of summarising a process in order to communicate it, is in a Process Block Diagram. This shows a process as a series of sub-processes across the top, with a vertical list of steps underneath, which themselves define each sub-process. Each sub-process leads to a tangible output which you can measure. (These measurable outputs will be useful for Rules 3 and 4). I recommend between three and eight sub-processes and a similar number of steps per sub-process. This breaks down your process to somewhere between 10 and 60 steps, depending on the complexity. The steps can be colour-coded to show which department or group is responsible. If more detail is required, the vertical steps of each sub-process can be placed across the top of another piece of paper and this sub-process then broken down further, using the same technique. An example of a whole-hospital process is given below.[107]

One of the most challenging aspects of creating this diagram is deciding on the sub-processes. There is no rule about where and how you sub-divide a process. However, I suggest that the most useful divisions are those where there is either a pause, a transfer or the completion of a document. For instance, waiting for test results, handing over a patient to another department, or filling in a form are all usually the end-points of a sub-process. Often it is the last of these which is most helpful, because the form itself is the output or result of the sub-process. We shall return to this in the next section.

FIGURE 13: Process Block Diagram

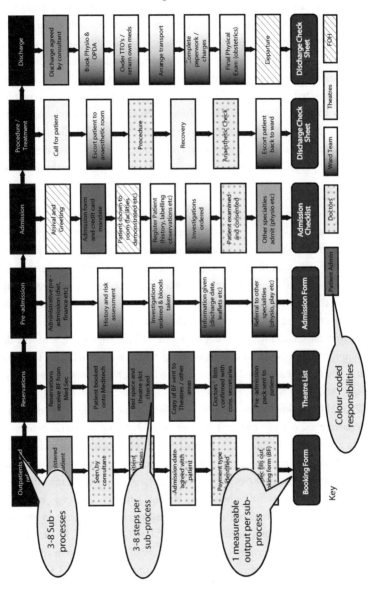

Columns (sub-processes): Outpatients and referral | Reservations | Pre-admission | Admission | Procedure / Treatment | Discharge

Outpatients and referral
- Registered patient
- Seen by consultant
- Patient investigations
- Admission date agreed with patient
- Payment type identified
- Sec fills out booking form (BF)
- **Booking Form**

Reservations
- Reservations receive BF from Med Sec
- Patient booked onto Meditech
- Bed space and theatre slot checked
- Copy of BF sent to Theatres / other areas
- Doctors' lists confirmed with cons secretaries
- Pre-admission pack sent to patient
- **Theatre List**

Pre-admission
- Administrative pre-admission (diet, finance etc)
- History and risk assessment
- Investigations ordered & bloods taken
- Information given (discharge date, leaflets etc)
- Referral to other specialities (physio, play etc)
- **Admission Form**

Admission
- Arrival and Greeting
- Admission form and credit card mandate
- Patient shown to room (facilities demonstrated etc)
- Register Patient (history, labelling observations etc)
- Investigations ordered
- Patient examined and consented
- Other specialties admit (physio etc)
- **Admission Checklist**

Procedure / Treatment
- Call for patient
- Escort patient to anaesthetic room
- Procedure
- Recovery
- Anaesthetic Check
- Escort patient back to ward
- **Discharge Check Sheet**

Discharge
- Discharge agreed by consultant
- Book Physio & OPDA
- Order TTO's / return own meds
- Arrange transport
- Complete paperwork / charges
- Final Physical Exam (obstetrics)
- Departure
- **Discharge Check Sheet**

Callouts:
- 3-8 Sub-processes
- 3-8 steps per sub-process
- 1 measureable output per sub-process
- Colour-coded responsibilities

Key: FoH | Theatres | Ward Team | Doctors | Patient Admin

PART TWO: Uniform

183

You can see from the above example that an enormous amount of complexity can be reduced to a single page. What we are not doing is providing details of every single decision point or possible combination, nor are we acknowledging the very likely variations between patients. In this case, we are providing an easily communicated, and easily displayed, summary of the patient journey. The alternative – a flow-chart with many different-sized boxes and decision points – is impossible to remember and is therefore largely useless. Using a Process Block diagram, we are acknowledging that the processes are largely managed intelligently by the people on the ground. It's not perfect, but these diagrams give context and clarity to people across the organisation on where their contribution lies.

Checklists

Let us now return to checklists. We have already recognised the enormous success of the WHO checklist in preventing unnecessary complications and death. It may now be more obvious why this simple device works so well. As well as many psychological benefits, most notably in flattening a hierarchy by making people more related, it also makes the processes more memorable. In fact, checklists are referred to as an aide-memoire in one London teaching hospital, precisely for this reason.[108]

Critically, checklists also act as a glue to hold together a fantastically complicated process that spans many organisational boundaries. The team in a theatre is composed of staff from many departments: anaesthetists, surgeons, scrub-nurses, anaesthetic nurses, radiographers, haematologists. What the checklist does so well is to bind these people from disparate departments, usually engaged in their individual departmental processes, into a single team managing a single process, namely the operation itself.

Checklists can be used in many areas where processes span organisational boundaries. Handover sheets (another term for checklist) are particularly useful when transferring patients between wards or during shift changes. Checklists can be used to encourage staff to perform an invasive procedure, such as a central line or catheter, in the correct manner.[109] There are many other applications. If you want to develop your own checklist, then you cannot do better than to read Atul Gawande's *Checklist Manifesto*.[110] He offers some useful guidance, which you can also read at the Project Check website [111] which, with a twist of self-reference, offers a checklist for developing checklists.

RULE 3: If you can't measure it, you can't manage it

One of the objections that I receive when talking about processes is "My leadership challenge isn't really about a process". My answer is that, at some point, it must be about a process if it has relevance to your leadership. It is possible that your challenge seems to be about people or behaviour. The idea of process may initially seem too rigorous or technical. My suggestion would be to ask the following key question: What measurable result is affected by this? The measurable result will be the output of a process. You can work backwards from there.

For example, one leader with whom I was working was concerned that the multi-disciplinary meetings she chaired did not have good attendance and documentation. The meetings were very ineffective and poorly structured. When I talked with her about it, she couldn't see that the meeting was really anything to do with a process. The meetings were to discuss the plans for the long-term patients under her care. They were looking at care plans and objectives for rehabilitation. But looking more widely she realised that the overall purpose of the meetings was to improve the speed and quality of the patient's recovery. The measurable outputs were related to these two factors: how quickly were her patients being rehabilitated and how did they feel about their progress.

She then realised that the meeting was actually a part of the management system (which we will discuss in the next section). To make the meeting more effective, she needed more data about the process being managed, namely the patient journey. That meant that the multi-disciplinary plans they were discussing needed to include more data about the speed and quality of the patient's recovery, not just about the plans they were making. Initially, the subject of process seemed dry and academic but she now saw that her meeting was about managing the quality of care and this was a subject about which she and her colleagues could become much more enthusiastic and committed.

The point here – and I've covered this in both the Committed and Active chapters – is that gathering data is the only way in which you can understand whether your process is working. And, just like in my story about Vanessa measuring accountable items, and the leader I mentioned above, we may need to install new mechanisms to gather the data that we need. I need to stress again that this is not about audit. We rely on audit so much in healthcare largely because we do not have IT systems which capture the information that we would like to monitor continuously. For proper process control, we need to find ways to measure both the number and quality of our processes each and every time they happen.

Once you have decided on your sub-processes and your outputs, as described in the section on Process Block Diagrams, you can then either count the outputs as they occur across time – giving you a measure of volume or activity – or you can measure the quality of the sub-process. The latter may be more difficult, although it may be enough to divide the outputs into a small number of categories. With Vanessa's accountable items, we were looking only for the slips which indicated that the counting process had not been done correctly. This is the simplest measure of quality: good versus bad. If this is too crude, you may want to divide your outputs into a wider range such as a patient satisfaction rating. Once you've done that, you can sub-divide these further, as you gain confidence and clarity.

If you don't already do it, measuring your process may sound onerous, but it's usually the implementation that is the tricky part. The actual counting doesn't usually take long.

EXERCISE 30: MEASURE YOUR PROCESS

Return to your leadership challenge and to the Process Block diagram you have created. Ensure that you are happy with the number and structure of the sub-processes that you have defined. There should be between three and eight. Ensure that you are clear about what outputs are produced by each sub-process. This should be a form or other physical item or computer record.

With your action team, decide what measures you want to put in place in order either to simply count these outputs or to determine their quality.

Agree on a mechanism for collecting this data.

RULE 4: You need a system to manage a process

Having defined, communicated and measured our process, we are in a good position, but it is not the end of the story. The WHO checklist has done a fabulous job of ensuring that we avoid both active and latent errors in theatre – but it has no impact on which patients have their surgery at what time, in what theatre, or which team members will be there. Similarly, we may have a process for prescribing, including an antibiotic prescribing policy – but this does not itself determine the contents of that policy. Or we may have an Occupational Therapy process – but that will not tell us whether the referrals are appropriate or the service is effective.

The decisions, changes and leadership activity that surround the process is the *management system*. A management system is:

> *... the collection of decision-making events along with their associated documents and information systems that is used to measure, monitor and make changes to a process and its resources.*

I have stood in the corridor of a surgical suite, next to a whiteboard, while two on-call surgeons, an on-call anaesthetist and a theatre manager dispute which of several emergency patients will be coming to theatre next. I work in an A&E department where a computer system monitors and displays the status of every patient in the department – it is also used to produce retrospective reports on performance. I have also been in the office of a secretary, who has shuffled through the referral letters of patients, modifying their appointments on the computer screen to balance the number of patients in each clinic. I have been in a clinical governance meeting where the level of weekend medical cover has been discussed.

All of these activities – some more haphazard than others – affect and modify the processes that are being undertaken. In general, then, a management system is a series of decision-making events, combined with documents, reports and other information that allows a process to be monitored and modified. Sometimes, the decision-making events are formal meetings but that may not always be the case. Executive diktat and, as with the secretary above, local modifications based on experience, may also play a part.

A good management system has clear decision-making meetings that look at the process in different time-scales and from different angles. It also has information flows that support those meetings. Much of the content of the Active chapter regarding meetings is highly applicable to management systems. The frequency of meetings, who attends, how much data is available and the quality of the conversations in those meetings are all relevant.

If we take the example of a patient-facing department then we usually see that there are a large number of meetings that influence how the overall process of the department functions. These may include shift handover meetings, departmental team meetings, senior leadership meetings, clinical governance meetings, nurse practice meetings, and financial and performance management meetings. Some of these meetings will be attended exclusively by members of the department to talk about staffing, clinical risk or performance. Others will be attended by people from other departments to discuss matters which touch other areas. This may include bed management meetings and directorate management meetings.

In addition to all those meetings, we also have management information systems which support the decisions made in those meetings. Some of these may be clinically based – monitoring patient flows through the department

– and some may be related to finance, quality, patient feedback, recruitment and so forth. Not all of these are computerised, but most are.

These two things together – the meeting structure and the information systems – should support each other to determine how effectively they control and modify the process of managing patients in the department. The two together create the D-A-D-A loop discussed in the Active chapter. The information systems create the Data and the Analysis. The meetings produce the Decisions and the Actions.

That's what is supposed to happen. However, management systems tend to grow ad-hoc around a process as it develops. We tend to install another meeting or design another spreadsheet without considering the whole. The meetings are often ineffective, for all the usual reasons, and the quality of the data can be poor. Consequently, many management systems duplicate effort, waste time and resources, produce poor decisions and are slow to accommodate changes both to the environment and to the needs of the process. This may in some measure be because the conceptual distinction between the process and the management system is not clear.

Management System Diagram

My solution to this problem is to use a mapping tool that creates a diagram which demonstrates the management system in its entirety.[112] This management system diagram is a simple grid. The rows are timescales in decreasing order: yearly, quarterly, monthly, weekly, daily and per-shift. The columns are functional areas – which will vary depending on the application. You should decide your own, but a good start may be to have columns titled: patients, staff, governance and performance.

Into each section of the grid, you should put the meetings that take place at that frequency in that functional area. Use a small cloud to represent a meeting. You can annotate each cloud with inputs, outputs and attendees. You should then draw lines between meetings that represent the information flow, showing how the outputs of one meeting feed the inputs of another. Finally, you will need to add elements to represent information systems such as computers or other means of recording or managing data.

Once completed, the diagram can then be used to critique the current management system. You should note where meetings overlap and where they are absent. It is also worth considering how long the process can continue without a decision-making meeting looking at the performance

---

of the process. This is sometimes called the interval of control. I sometimes use the analogy of checking your bank account. Too frequent and you waste time reviewing things that are not changing, too infrequent and you may miss something important.

After critiquing the current system, a new improved system can be drawn up using the same technique and then be agreed between the players. It can then be used as a communication device to explain how the new system will work and ensure that everyone understands how and where decisions are made.

Below is an example diagram. The detail is not intended to be readable, but the overall shape should give you an idea of what the diagram should look like. The amount of detail in such a diagram can make it difficult to read, so for added impact, you can use a wall covered with brown paper, to map this out at a more human scale.[113]

Figure 14: Management Reporting System diagram

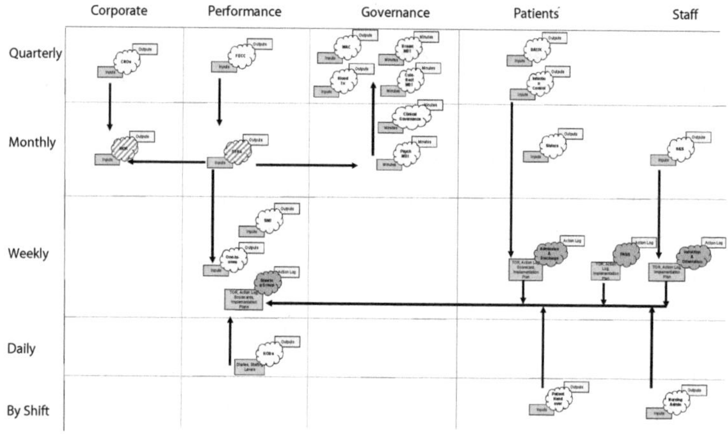

This chapter has summarised, as briefly as possible, the importance of processes and some key ideas and models for improving them. Once you have a handle on your process and its performance, you will are close to the end of the CAREFUL framework. You will, I hope, have put people before process and developed a system that can monitor and improve performance using a team that is happy and motivated.

My view is that in this position, you can go far …

EXERCISE 31: MEASURE YOUR PROCESS

Return to your leadership challenge and to the Process Block diagram you have created. Ensure that you are happy with the number and structure of the sub-processes that you have defined. There should be between three and eight. Ensure that you are clear about what outputs are produced by each sub-process. This should be a form or other physical item or computer record.

With your action team, decide what measures you want to put in place in order to either simply count these outputs or to determine their quality.

Agree a mechanism for collecting this data.

EXERCISE 32: MAP YOUR MANAGEMENT SYSTEM

For your leadership challenge, draw the management system diagram showing how the system currently works:

- What are the decision-making meetings – whether formal or informal – that you currently use to manage your process?
- How often do these occur, what inputs are used and what outputs produced?
- Into what categories (columns) do these meetings fall?
- How do these decision-making meetings link with the information systems?
- How does information flow between the meetings? How do they link?
- With your action team, review the current management system and decide what changes may be necessary. Look for areas of overlap, where more than one meeting may cover the same ground, and look for gaps, where no meetings exist. Are these gaps filled by informal decision making? Would that be better undertaken with a formal meeting?
- Draw out a new diagram and engage your audience in this proposed management system.
- To improve the meetings within the system, return to the Active chapter and review the DADA loop, the Kantor models and the four noble tools.

LEADING
Aim for the top

All anyone asks for is a chance to work for pride.

– W Edwards Deming

On 23 November 2004, Mrs Mary L McClinton died in a hospital in the state of Washington, USA. She was 69. The cause of her death was a mix up between different solutions in an operating theatre and she was fatally injected with Chlorhexidine, a powerfully toxic antiseptic. The reaction of the hospital was to admit liability and make a full disclosure. But they went beyond that. Mrs McClinton's untimely death was the galvanising event which turned an otherwise normal hospital into a world leader in safety. The leaders of the hospital decided that if they could not assure the safety of their patients they should not be in business. They took lessons from the manufacturing sector and adopted the tenets of the Toyota Production System (TPS), a system of quality improvement made famous in the middle of the 20th century for putting the Japanese car industry ahead of its American rivals.[114]

The hospital in question is Virginia Mason Medical Center in Seattle. In the last decade it has spawned many imitators and even set up its own consulting arm, the Virginia Mason Institute, to promote it's now famous Virginia Mason Production System (VMPS) across the world. Part of the legacy of this transformation is the Mary L McClinton Patient Safety Award, the hospital's highest accolade for improvements in patient safety.

At the time of writing, Virginia Mason had garnered numerous awards for its work. From HealthGrades alone, it has won a Stroke Care

Excellence award, a Pulmonary Care Excellence award, a Cardiac Care Excellence award, as well as a Distinguished Hospital Award for Clinical Excellence three years in a row, America's 100 Best Hospitals Award for two years in a row. They have also landed America's 100 Best Hospitals Award for Critical Care, Gastroenterology and General Surgery – each for three years in a row. Further they received, for three years in a row, an Outstanding Patient Experience Award. To put that in perspective, there are 5,686 hospitals in America. They have achieved a position in the top one to two per cent in all six categories for three years in a row.

How did they do this? In some ways it was simple: the leaders of the hospital decided that they were going to become the safest hospital on the planet and followed through on that commitment. It is arguable, given their statistics, that they have achieved that ambition. And, although the journey wasn't easy, they retained the commitment of the leadership team throughout. Having achieved this level of safety, they are not complacent. They want to improve further – and to advocate their experience in order to help us all achieve these levels of excellence. In time, it is possible that the VMPS will do for healthcare what the Toyota Production System did for car manufacturing.

You may be reading this thinking: sadly, I do not work for such an enlightened organisation. Like most healthcare leaders, I work for a second-rate organisation that is – like much of healthcare – content with impoverished levels of ambition, unacceptable levels of patient harm and the provision of an often terrible patient experience. I am just a small cog in a poorly oiled machine.

To counter this position, I'd like to retell an apocryphal story about John F Kennedy and a cleaner. In this urban myth, Kennedy visited the NASA Apollo space programme in the early 1960s and talked to a member of the cleaning staff asking him: "What's your job?" The cleaner's famous reply: "My job, Sir, is to put a man on the moon!" What makes this anecdote interesting is not its veracity but its persistence. There is little likelihood that this is true, partly because the story is told about other dignitaries in other situations, and partly because – well, why on earth would anyone ask a cleaner what his job was? And yet the story continues to be told and retold, often by management consultant types like me. Why? I think it is because we want it to be true. We want it to be possible, in some ideal world, for the goals of a large organisation to filter down to everyone, no matter how mundane their job, in a simple, pithy statement that makes our hairs stand on end. If only, we think, it were possible to inspire the cleaning and catering staff in our hospitals to answer, when asked what their job was, "I'm saving lives, Sir!". The reason we retell the Kennedy cleaner story is not because we think it's true either then or now, but because – as Deming suggests in the quote above – we want it to be true *for ourselves*.

I don't know if working for Virginia Mason is like that. But I can vouch for the fact that it is not like that in any healthcare institution for which I have worked. In fact it personally grieves me to know that, when I am treating patients, I am working in an organisation that continues to perpetrate avoidable harm and I am maddened by the inertia that surrounds this. I know we can do better.

Instead, I personally want to work for an organisation that is first-or-best. I want to be proud of the organisation for which I work. This book is written largely because I believe you feel the same way.

This short, final chapter is therefore something of a call to arms. I would exhort you to abandon any negative view you may hold that you are simply a cog in a failing machine and that you work for leaders who are insipid, stupid or lazy. If you want to work for an organisation that is first-or-best, then you need to strive for that yourself. You need to adapt your ambition accordingly, to come clean and declare your wish to be first-or-best.

Negativity will get you nowhere. Instead, as a leader, you need to use all the techniques and models in this book – and any other systems of improvement you find helpful – in order to create an environment where your staff can take pride in the work they do for patients.

In the Committed chapter, I made passing reference to the idea of a first-or-best position. There are a few healthcare organisations in the UK that can reasonably argue that they have such a position. My own, highly subjective list includes Stoke Mandeville (Spinal Injuries), Imperial (Academic Research), The Maudsley (Psychiatry), The Marsden (Oncology), Great Ormond Street (Children) and Kings College Hospital (Trauma). When I reflect on this list, and the enthusiasm I hear from colleagues who want to work there, it's clear that if an organisation can find this first-or-best position, they can attract and retain staff on the strength of the reputation it creates. This creates a self-reinforcing, positive cycle of reputation, staff retention and quality.

But my point is that this doesn't have to be at an organisational level. It can exist at a departmental or team level too. Prof, my recently retired colleague whose story started this book, didn't work for an organisation that was demonstrably first-or-best. But he created a critical care unit that was.

My assertion is that by adopting a position of first-or-best, you personally can develop a cycle of reputation, staff retention and quality. You don't need to attempt to become the safest hospital in the world. That position is taken – and won't be given up lightly. You can, however, be the first team to receive a national award, the first department to achieve an outstanding rating from your regulator, the safest team in your hospital, the clinic with the best patient experience feedback in your region, the first department to be fully paper-free, the highest quality service, the safest theatres. The list is endless. The opportunities are all yours. The leadership challenge I have encouraged you to work through in this book can be the first step to delivering such a first-or-best position.

It is with this hope that I end this book. I hope that you – and all your fellow healthcare leaders – will rise to this challenge of delivering a service which is first-or-best. By such small, yet significant, increments, using your energy and skill, we can thereby motivate all our healthcare teams to excel in serving our patients. We can – and will – create a better world from the bottom up, rather than wait for instructions from the top.

Remember: you're not stuck in traffic. You *are* the traffic.

You are not hamstrung by the leadership. You *are* the leadership.

Notes

1   Message by Nelson Mandela at the "Healing and Reconciliation Service, dedicated to HIV/AIDS sufferers & The Healing of Our Land", 6 December 2000. *http://db.nelsonmandela.org/speeches pub_view. asp?pg=item&ItemID=NMS967*. Retrieved Feb. 2016.

2   The NHS in the UK has a widely publicised leadership framework. The CAREFUL model is intended to support and complement this and similar models by providing a mnemonic and practical advice particularly around *personal qualities* and *improving the service*.

3   For some examples, see Moody, 1973; Maben, Latter and Clark, 2007; Laschinger, Wong and Grau, 2012.

4   I have included exercises when I feel they would be practically useful in helping to cement the concepts and ideas that I present in the main text. The exercises are not intended to be patronising. If you find them so, please ignore them. I hope their benefit outweighs any intrusion they may cause to the body of the text.

5   I am grateful to Andrew Wells of One Point Three for this pair of insightful questions (*one.point.three.com*)

6   From *The Prince*, by Nicolo Machiavelli, Chapter VI, Translated by W K Marriott. From *http://www.gutenberg.org/files/1232/1232-h/1232-h.htm*. Retrieved Feb. 2016 .

7   *As you like it*, William Shakespeare, Act II Scene VII.

8   This is partially in deference to Max De Pree's deep and penetrating book *Leadership is an Art* (De Pree, 1989).

9   *http://www.anlp.org/presuppositions-of-nlp*. Retrieved Feb. 2016 .

10   This is an adage within the practice of Neuro-Linguistic Programming, or NLP, a branch of practical psychology pioneered in the USA in the 1970s. The basis of NLP is that neural processes, linguistic structures, and behavioural habits are all interconnected, and that it is possible to intervene in patterns of both thought and behaviour by modifying the language that we use to describe the situations in which we find ourselves.

11   Jerome Groopman's book *How Doctors Think* (Groopman, 2007) is a somewhat depressing read for those of us who would like to think we can be consistently right in our clinical judgments.

12   See also the section on Negative Assertion in the Focussed chapter.

13   Covey, 1989.

14   Bateson, 1972 p. 143.

15   The elephant and rider model (Heath and Heath, 2011) was originally put forward by Jonathan Haidt, Professor of Ethical Leadership

at New York's Stern School of Business, in his book *The Happiness Hypothesis* (Haidt, 2006).

16 Peters, 2011.

17 First coined by Daniel Goleman (Goleman, 1995).

18 Alimo-Metcalfe and Alban-Metcalfe (2001) found in a survey of over 2,000 healthcare leaders that they had consistently higher opinions of themselves than either their immediate supervisors or those they managed. On the balance of probabilities, you are not as popular as you think.

19 The ratio borne out by John Gottman's extensive research (The Gottman Institute, 2016; Gottman and Gottman, 2013) into successful marriages, but is also supported by quantitative analysis into team dynamics (Losada and Heaphy, 2004). In all cases, negativity outweighs positivity in our memories (Baumeister et al., 2001).

20 For a beautiful, profound and poetic examination of this, I would highly recommend *The Tao of Leadership* (Heider and Laozi, 1985).

21 While this quote is widely attributed to Maya Angelou, it is likely from an earlier source see *https://quoteinvestigator.com/2014/04/06/they-feel/* .

22 Studer, 2003.

23 You may also hear the phrase "blame culture". Used accurately, this phrase refers to an environment where individuals are held accountable for systemic failures and where mistakes are treated differently depending on the outcome. This is a dangerous, albeit common, situation which we discuss in more detail in the Responsive chapter.

24 The three ideas in this chapter are influenced by the work of Quint Studer and Studer Group: *www.studergroup.com*.

25 Attributed to a memory of his nephew, Billy James, in 1902; quoted in Leon Edel, *Henry James: The Master 1901–1916*, Vol v: (1972), p. 124.

26 In case you have difficulty imagining what it might be like to die of thirst, here's a brief extract from Nathaniel Philbrick's book *In the Heart of the Sea* (Philbrick, 2000):

In the "cotton-mouth" phase of thirst, saliva becomes thick and foul-tasting; the tongue clings irritatingly to the teeth and the roof of the mouth. Even though speech is difficult sufferers are often moved to complain ceaselessly about their thirst until their voices become so cracked and hoarse that they can speak no more. A lump seems to form in the throat, causing the sufferer to swallow repeatedly in a vain attempt to dislodge it. Severe pain is felt in the head and neck. The face feels full due to the shrinking of the skin. Hearing is affected, and many people begin to hallucinate.

27 I have been privileged to be party to the evolution of these ideas over several years, and I am pleased to be able to present here, in anticipation of Andy's forthcoming book *The Care Ethic*. The opening story of this chapter is derived from Andy's work and is used gratefully with permission.

28 Michael Tomasello, quoted in Haidt (2012). See: *http://tannerlectures.utah.edu/_documents/a-to-z/t/Tomasello_08.pdf* .

29 "To fail to attend to the promotion of kinship, connectedness and kindness between staff and with patients is to fail to address a key dimension of what makes people do well for others." (Ballat, 2007).

30 Recent neuroscience research shows that this is a capacity common to most humans from an early age. Mirror neurons fire when we perform a particular act and when we observe someone else doing the same thing, so that it "mirrors" the behaviours of others, and may be the basis for learning and understanding others.

31 This is often referred to as The Law of the Prophets, from the New Testament Bible, Matthew 7:12.

32 See Menzies, 1960, discussed in more detail in the Focused chapter.

33 See national reports on poor sleeping habits and their deleterious effects: *http://www.ncbi.nlm.nih.gov/books/NBK19948/*.

34 As W Edwards Deming, arguably the greatest thinker on management and leadership, said: "Whenever there is fear, you will get wrong figures."

35 Maben, Latter and Clark, 2007; Moody, 1973; Johnson, Haigh and Yates-Bolton, 2007; Kivimaki, 2001.

36 *http://www.theschwartzcenter.org/media/patient_story.pdf*.

37 Participant quote, at: *http://www.theschwartzcenter.org/supporting-caregivers/schwartz-center-rounds/*. Retrieved July 2015.

38 Lown and Manning, 2010.

39 One of the most powerful testaments to this is quoted by Malcolm Gladwell in his book *Blink* (Gladwell, 2005). "What comes up again and again in malpractice cases is that patients say they were rushed or ignored or treated poorly. 'People just don't sue doctors they like.'"

40 There are many references I could quote here, but the two best are Youngson, 2010 and Lown, 1996.

41 Youngson, 2010. *http://www.heartsinhealthcare.com*.

42 WH Murray, *The Scottish Himalaya Expedition*, Dent, 1951, p. 7.

43 There is a good description of this in Hallina, 2009.

44 *http://www.tfri.ca/en/aboutus/terry-fox.aspx*.

45 We watched Beth's Story, one of many at *www.patientstories.org.uk*.

46 Despite the lack of elephant-motivating context for this target, most people recognise that the focus on waiting times has been a key factor in raising standards of emergency medicine in the UK.

47   The book (Cialdini, 2001) is filled with fascinating and often disturbing research. His ideas reflect Gregory Bateson (Bateson, 1972), quoted in the Introduction, who believed that our unconscious habits drive much of our behaviour.

48   Milgram, 1963.

49   *A little more conversation, a little more action*, from the film *Live a little, Love a little,* written by Mac Davis and Billy Strange, RCA, 1968 From the film *Live a little, Love a little,* written by Mac Davis and Billy Strange, RCA, 1968.

50   From an address at the Second Assembly of the World Council of Churches, Evanston, Illinois, 19 Aug. 1954, see *http://www.presidency.ucsb.edu/ws/?pid=9991.*

51   Allen, 2001.

52   The full quotation, from Moltke the elder, a nineteenth-century Prussian military strategist translates as: "No plan of operations extends with certainty beyond the first encounter with the enemy's main strength".

53   You can use whatever term you prefer – Action Team, Task and Finish group – but I recommend you avoid the word committee. Committees have a poor reputation for getting things done.

54   Having a shared action-management system is essential for your meetings. It can also be very useful for one-to-one coaching sessions, which we will discuss in the Energetic chapter.

55   I have found no clear references to the origin of this model. I was taught it when working for Cambridge Management Consultants (latterly Celerant Consulting).

56   See *www.kantorinstitute.com.* Kantor, 2012.

57   Decision-making meetings are one of many types of meeting. They are the most difficult to run, which is why I spend so much time talking about them. I describe other types of meeting in other chapters.

58   All of these are available to download at www.careful.cc.

59   I treat the word *data* as singular, like agenda. It feels more natural to me, even though I recognise it's not yet decided. See *http://www.theguardian.com/guardian–observer–style–guide–d* and *http://www.economist.com/style–guide/singular–or–plural.*

60   http://dilbert.com/strip/2003-10-07.

61   Reason, 2000.

62   The most egregious example of this is of Julie Thao, charged with manslaughter over a simple drug error. See "Chasing Zero", from minute 22:40, available at *https://www.youtube.com/watch?v=MtSbgUuXdaw.* Retrieved Aug. 2015.

63   We may also identify two other unsafe acts: recklessness and professional negligence. This book cannot hope to cover these two, very rare, instances. For the sake of brevity, we will count only errors and violations as unsafe acts.

64 Vincent, 2010.

65 The incident is dramatised in the NHS video "Safe Administration of Intrathecal Chemotherapy" *https://www.youtube.com/watch?v=oNCObzqSMa0*. Retrieved Aug. 2015 [accessed 1 Aug. 2022].

66 It is tempting to believe that electronic prescribing would solve these problems completely. Although it does reduce the risk of adverse events, it comes with its own problems and opportunities for error. See Schnipper, 2016.

67 The Wagon Wheel methodology is presented with permission of Joanne Haswell and Kate Hill from Inpractice Training *http://www.inpracticetraining.com/investigations/* .

68 In March 2015, NHS England changed their guidance on SIs to include potential harm as a reason for a full investigation. The guidance is comprehensive *http://www.england.nhs.uk* Retrieved Aug. 2015.

69 Dekker, 2014.

70 Technically, these are barrier analysis diagrams. But Wagon Wheels is a much better term, I'm sure you'll agree.

71 Presentation given at *A Question of Quality* conference, London, 25 February 2016, Barbican, London.

72 Cooperrider and Srivastva, 1987.

73 By tradition, even where the usual spelling is *enquiry*, AI keeps the American spelling of its originators.

74 A celebrated recent example where AI has worked in a healthcare setting is at the University of Virginia Health System has been written up in useful introduction to AI, it contains lists of example questions for use in different circumstances. See May, 2011.

75 Lynch, 2006.

76 Menlo Innovations, described by Richard Sheridan in *Joy, Inc.* (Sheridan, 2013), seems to parallel this atmosphere.

77 Alimo-Metcalfe and Alban-Metcalfe, 2001; Alimo-Metcalfe and Alban-Metcalfe, 2005.

78 The others were as follows (I have added in brackets the correlating ideas from this book): valuing individuals (kindness); networking and achieving (commitment from others, completing actions); enabling (developing your team); being accessible (having Golden Quadrant time); being decisive (having focus).

79 McKernan's relentless pursuit of authenticity has wider application. Looking back on "The Troubles" it is easy to see the entire catastrophe is formed by mistrust based on a lack of relatedness – in this case going back many generations. The same is true in the breakdown of a marriage. Relatedness disappears. In both these examples it becomes difficult not only to work together, but to live together.

80 I offer this model only as a guide. It may differ from some similar models you are already familiar. It shares a great deal with "Situational Leadership" popularised by Hershey and Blanchard and discussed in more detail later in this chapter. I am not qualified to comment on their relative merits. I use this version only because it makes the most sense to me in my own leadership roles, and when working with other healthcare leaders.

81 This model is reproduced with permission of Evolve Management Partners LLP, from the *Evolve Handbook*, Version 1.4.

82 Sleepy Hollow is, in fact, suffused with Fixation – one of the three F's. I think this makes it more understandable why bureaucracies, where norming teams predominate, behave so unkindly.

83 The word coachee is so ugly I avoid it at all costs.

84 The Red Arrow display teams are often cited as being an exemplar of a performing team, its ex-members often use their experience to describe this stage of team development to less fortunate groups. It is easy to forget that an enormous amount of forming, storming and norming is needed before any group of human beings can perform at that level.

85 A more colourful term is coined by Robert Sutton in his book *The No Asshole Rule*. He defines intolerable behaviour more narrowly as being more humiliating, directly disrespectful, power-based and aggressive. If you have an asshole problem, not just a Negatives problem, his book will help more than this chapter.

86 I mentioned this story briefly in the Committed chapter.

87 *https://www.gov.uk*

88 2013 figures: 303.7 billion vehicle mile; 1713 KSI casualties; circumference of earth at the equator; 24,902 miles.

89 *http://www.gmc-uk.org/guidance/good_medical_practice.asp.*

90 An example of this can be found on *www.careful.cc* website.

91 The NHS is sadly fraught with such conversations. I am convinced, having read the Francis Report, that the Mid-Staffordshire scandal was largely brought about by parent–child conversations at all levels of the healthcare system. It could be argued that the hospital, regional health authority and regulator all became involved in a complex, multi-layered and catastrophic psycho-social game to avoid facing the reality of a failing hospital.

92 A recent All Party Parliamentary Group in the UK recommended mindfulness should be incorporated into government policy in health, education and the criminal justice system. (Hyland, 2016).

93 I recommend The Meditation Handbook: The Practical Guide to Eastern and Western Meditation Techniques by David Fontana for an

excellent and fascinating overview of the subject from a both practical and theoretical point of view.

94   There can be confusion between mindfulness and meditation. Mindfulness is the English translation of the pali term *sati* (Sanskrit *smr.ti*) which means recollection or remembering. Mindfulness is a mental faculty. The capacity to remember or remind yourself of what you are doing. To sit mindfully is to sit while continuously remembering that you are sitting. It is sometimes related to a rope – which ties your attention to an object. Meditation (the English translation of the Pali *jhana*, Sanskrit *dhya*) is the act of sitting (or sometimes walking, lying or standing) while contemplating in some way, or practicing a technique – of which mindfulness of breathing is a common example (Brasington, 2015). Meditation is like practising music, but training the mind rather than the fingers and ears. Meditation practice is not possible without a good deal of mindfulness.

95   See *Wherever You Go, There You Are: Mindfulness meditation for everyday life,* Jon Kabat Zin, 2004.

96   See *Doing Time Doing Vipassana.* (1997). [film] Israel: Eilona Ariel, Ayelet Menahemi.

97   David Lynch, *Catching the Big Fish.*

98   If you don't believe me, there is decades of research to back-up all these assertions. An extensive list of studies can be found at *https://www.researchforwellness.com/mindfulness.*

99   Gawande, 2010.

100   One case of wrong site surgery, both infamous and tragic, occurred in Bristol in the 1990s when a patient's sole functioning kidney was removed instead of his diseased one, hastening his death. A medical student spotted that the X-ray on the wall was the wrong way round and voiced concerns but was ignored. The WHO checklist would likely have avoided this error because it insists that all members of the team are recognised at the beginning of the list, which creates more relatedness, flattens the hierarchy and gives permission for people to challenge each other.

101   Gareth Morgan's highly readable book *Images of Organization* provides an excellent overview of organisational theory using metaphors (Morgan, 1986).

102   There is a quality improvement approach, promoted heavily by GE, called Six Sigma. This is an to make attempt processes so robust that the chance of an error occurring is related to six standard deviations from the mean – i.e. about one in 3.4 million risk. Success in implementing the Six Sigma approach is one of the reasons that you almost never receive a faulty smartphone, and why almost all cars coming out of a modern production facility will run without problem. It is why aircraft hardly ever fall out of the sky.

103 Until recently, healthcare invested less than any other sector in IT – except mining. Thankfully that is changing. See *http://www.economist.com/node/13437990*.

104 This variation itself is a contributory factor in the lack of good quality IT.

105 See Dekker, 2014, for a full explanation of how unsafe systems are kept safe by users.

106 You may do both, of course. Leaders with clinical responsibilities may also deliver the service. For the sake of argument I'm discussing your leadership responsibilities.

107 Templates for Process Block Diagrams and other material can be found at *www.careful.cc*.

108 The term helps overcome some of the resistance to the term "checklist", which for some people has negative connotations, suggesting a reduction in flexibility and therefore clinical judgment.

109 A checklist had a part to play in reducing central-line infections in the Matching Michigan programme. See *http://qualitysafety.bmj.com/content/early/2012/09/20/bmjqs-2012-001325.full* and *http://qualitysafety.bmj.com/content/22/2/93.full*.

110 Gawande, 2010.

111 *www.projectcheck.org/checklists.html*. Retrieved Jan. 2016.

112 I am grateful for my time with Celerant Consulting (now part of Hitachi) from whose Management Control and Reporting System (MCRS) concept this is derived.

113 A photograph of such a brown paper exercise can be found at *www.careful.cc*.

114 The Toyota Production System is based in large part on the work of W Edwards Deming, who I have quoted at the beginning of this chapter and elsewhere.

References

Adams, S. (2000). *Random Acts of Management*. London: Boxtree.

Alimo-Metcalfe, B. and Alban-Metcalfe, R. (2001). The development of a new Transformational Leadership Questionnaire. *Journal of Occupational and Organizational Psychology*, 74(1), pp. 1–27.

Alimo-Metcalfe, B. and Alban-Metcalfe, J. (2005). Leadership: Time for a New Direction?. Leadership, [online] 1(1), pp. 51–71. Available at: *http://www.ctrtraining.co.uk/documents/ AlimoMetcalfeLeadershipTimeforaNewDirection.pdf*) [accessed 23 Jan. 2016.

Allen, D. (2001). *Getting Things Done*. New York: Viking.

Ballatt, J. (2011). *Intelligent Kindness*. London: RCPsych Publications.

Bateson, G. (1972). *Steps to an Ecology of Mind*. San Francisco: Chandler Pub. Co.

Baumeister, R., Bratslavsky, E., Finkenauer, C. and Vohs, K. (2001). Bad is stronger than good. *Review of General Psychology*, 5(4), pp. 323–370.

Beckhard, R. (1972). Optimizing team-building efforts, *Journal of contemporary business*, Vol. 1.1972, 3, pp. 23–32.

Berne, E. (1964). *Games People Play – The Basic Hand Book of Transactional Analysis*. New York: Ballantine Books.

Brasington, L. (2015). *Right Concentration*. Boston and London: Shambala.

Bunker, B. and Alban, B. (1997). *Large Group Interventions*. San Francisco: Jossey-Bass.

Cialdini, R. (2001). *Influence*. Boston, MA: Allyn and Bacon.

Collins, J. (2001). *Good to Great*. New York, NY: HarperBusiness.

Cooperrider, D. and Srivastva, S. (1987). Appreciative Inquiry In Organizational Life. *Research in Organizational Change and Development*, [online] 1, pp. 129–169. Available at: *http://www. centerforappreciativeinquiry.net/wp-content/uploads/2012/05/ APPRECIATIVE_INQUIRY_IN_Orgnizational_life.pdf* [accessed 17 Jan. 2016].

Covey, S. (1989). *The Seven Habits of Highly Effective People*. New York: Simon and Schuster.

De Pree, M. (1989). *Leadership is an Art*. New York: Doubleday.

Dekker, S. (2014). *The Field Guide to Understanding "Human Error"*. 3rd ed. Farnham: Ashgate Publishing Ltd.

Doing Time, Doing Vipassana. (1997). [film] Israel: Eilona Ariel, Ayelet Menahemi.

Fontana, D. (2010). *The Meditation Handbook*. London: Watkins.

Gawande, A. (2010). *The Checklist Manifesto*. New York: Metropolitan Books.

General Medical Council, (2016). *GMC | Good Medical Practice (2013)*. [online] *gmc-uk.org*. Available at: *http://www.gmc-uk.org/guidance/ good_medical_practice.asp* [accessed 17 Jan. 2016].

Gilbert, P. (2009). *The Compassionate Mind*. London: Constable and Robinson.

Gladwell, M. (2005). *Blink*. New York: Little, Brown and Company.

Goleman, D. (1995). *Emotional Intelligence*. New York: Bantam Books.

Gottman, J. and Gottman, J. (2013). *The Empirical Basis of Gottman Couples Therapy*. 1st ed. [ebook] The Gottman Institute. Available at: *https://www.gottman.com/wp-content/uploads/EmpiricalBasis-Update3.pdf* [accessed 5 Jan. 2016].

Groopman, J. (2007). *How doctors Think*. Boston: Houghton Mifflin.

Haidt, J. (2006). *The happiness Hypothesis*. New York: Basic Books.

Haidt, J. (2012). *The righteous Mind*. New York: Pantheon Books.

Hallinan, J. (2009). *Why We Make Mistakes*. New York: Broadway Books.

Heath, C. and Heath, D. (2011). *Switch*. London: Random House Business.

Heath, C. and Heath, D. (2013). *Decisive: How to Make Better Decisions*. New York: Random House.

Hersey, P. and Blanchard, K. H. (1977). *Management of organizational behavior: Utilizing Human Resources*. 3rd ed. Englewood Cliffs, N.J.: Prentice-Hall.

Hyland, T. (2016). Mindful Nation UK Report by the Mindfulness All-Party Parliamentary Group (MAPPG). *Journal of Vocational Education & Training*, [online] pp. 1–4. Available at: *https://www. themindfulnessinitiative.org/mindful-nation-report* [Accessed Jan. 2016].

Johnson, M., Haigh, C. and Yates-Bolton, N. (2007). Valuing of altruism and honesty in nursing students: a two-decade replication study. *J. Adv Nurs*, 57(4), pp. 366–374.

Kabat-Zinn, J. (1994). *Wherever You Go, There You Are*. New York: Hyperion.

Kantor, D. (2012). *Reading the Room*. San Francisco, Jossey-Bass.

Kivimäki, M., Sutinen, R., Elovainio, M., Vahtera, J., Räsänen, K., Töyry, S., Ferrie, J.E. and Firth-Cozens, J. (2001). Sickness absence in hospital physicians: 2 year follow up study on determinants. *Occupational and Environmental Medicine*, 58(6), pp. 361–366.

Laing, R. (1972). *Knots*. London: Vintage.

Landsberg, M. (2003). *The Tao of Coaching: Boost your effectiveness at work by inspiring and developing those around you*. London: Profile Books.

Laschinger, H., Wong, C. and Grau, A. (2012). Authentic leadership, empower-ment and burnout: a comparison in new graduates and experienced nurses. *Journal of Nursing Management*, 21(3), pp. 541–552.

Losada, M. and Heaphy, E. (2004). The Role of Positivity and Connectivity in the Performance of Business Teams: A Nonlinear Dynamics Model. *American Behavioural Scientist*, 47(6), pp. 740–765.

Lown, B. (1996). *The Lost Art of Healing*. Boston: Houghton Mifflin.

Lown, B. and Manning, C. (2010). The Schwartz Center Rounds: Evaluation of an Interdisciplinary Approach to Enhancing Patient-Centered Communication, Teamwork, and Provider Support. *Academic Medicine*, [online] 85(6), pp. 1073–1081. Available at: *http://journals.lww.com/academicmedicine/Fulltext/2010/06000/ The_Schwartz_Center_Rounds__Evaluation_of_an.37.aspx* [accessed 17 Jan. 2016].

Lynch, D. (2006). *Catching the Big Fish*. New York: Tarcher/Penguin.

Maben, J., Latter, S. and Clark, J. (2007). The sustainability of ideals, values and the nursing mandate: evidence from a longitudinal qualitative study. *Nurs Inq*, 14(2), pp. 99–113.

Marsh, H. (2014). *Do No Harm*. London: Weidenfeld &Nicholson.

May, N., Becker, D. and Frankel, R. (2011). *Appreciative Inquiry in Healthcare*. Brunswick, Ohio: Crown Custom Publishing.

Menzies, I. (1960). A Case-Study in the Functioning of Social Systems as a Defence against Anxiety: A Report on a Study of the Nursing Service of a General Hospital. *Human Relations*, 13(2), pp. 95–121.

Milgram, S. (1963). Behavioral Study of obedience. *The Journal of Abnormal and Social Psychology*, 67(4), pp. 371–378.

Moody, P. (1973). Attitudes of cynicism and humanitarianism in nursing students and staff nurses. *Journal of Nursing Education*, 12(3), pp. 9–13.

Morgan, G. (1986). *Images of Organization*. Beverly Hills: Sage Publications.

Peters, S. (2011). *The Chimp Paradox*. London: Vermilion.

Philbrick, N. (2000). *In the Heart of the Sea*. New York: Viking.

Reason, J. (2000). Human error: models and management. *BMJ*, [online] 320(7237), pp. 768–770. Available at: *http://www.bmj.com/content/320/7237/768* [accessed 17 Jan. 2016].

Reason, J. (2008). *The Human Contribution*. Farnham, England: Ashgate.

Schnipper, J. (2016). Free-Text Notes as a Marker of Needed Improvements in Electronic Prescribing. *JAMA Internal Medicine. http://archinte.jamanetwork.com/article.aspx?articleid=2498842*.

Schwartz, K. (1995). A patient's story. *The Boston Globe magazine*. [online] Available at: *https://www.bostonglobe.com/magazine/1995/07/16/patient-story/q8ihHg8LfyinPA25Tg5JRN/story.html* [accessed 17 Jan. 2016].

Sheridan, R. (2013). *Joy, Inc*. London: Portfolio: Penguin.

Smith, M. (1975). *When I Say No, I Feel Guilty*. New York: Dial Press.

Studer, Q. (2003). *Hardwiring Excellence*. Gulf Breeze, FL: Fire Starter.

Sutton, R. (2007). *The No Asshole Rule*. New York: Warner Business Books.

The Gottman Institute, (2016). *Home – The Gottman Institute*. [online] Available at: *https://www.gottman.com* [accessed 5 Jan. 2016].

The Official Highway Code. (2007). London: Stationery Office Books.

UK Government, (2013). *Report of the Mid Staffordshire NHS Foundation Trust Public Inquiry (Francis Report)*. [online] London: TSO. Available at: *https://www.gov.uk/government/publications/report-of-the-mid-staffordshire-nhs-foundation-trust-public-inquiry* [accessed 17 Jan. 2016].

Vincent, C. (2010). *Patient Safety*. Chichester, West Sussex: Wiley-Blackwell.

Youngson, R. (2012). *Time to Care*. Raglan, NZ: Rebelheart Publishers.